Carnegie Learning Integrated Math III

Student Edition
Volume 1
3rd Edition

David Dengler
Sandy Bartle Finocchi
William S. Hadley
Mary Lou Metz

Carnegie Learning >

Pittsburgh, Pennsylvania

Carnegie Learning >

437 Grant St., Suite 1906
Pittsburgh, PA 15219
Phone 888.851.7094
Customer Service Phone 888.851.7094, option 3

www.carnegielearning.com

Printing History
First Edition 2013
Second Edition 2014
Third Edition 2015

ISBN: 978-1-60972-668-3
Set ISBN: 978-1-60972-234-0

Printed in the United States of America by Cenveo Corporation
1 2 3 4 5 6 7 8 9 CC 18 17 16 15

Dear Student,

You are about to begin an exciting endeavor using mathematics! To be successful, you will need the right tools. This book is one of the most important tools you will use this year. Throughout this book there is space for note-taking, sketching, and calculating. You will be given opportunities to think and reason about various mathematical concepts and use tools such as tables, graphs, and graphing calculators.

This year you will face many new challenges both in and outside of the classroom. While some challenges may seem difficult, it is important to remember that effort matters. You must realize that it may take hard work and perseverance to succeed—and your hard work will pay off!

Connections in mathematics are important. Throughout this text, you will build new knowledge based upon your prior knowledge. It is our goal that you see mathematics as relevant because it provides a common and useful language for discussing and solving real-world problems.

I bet the folks at home would like to know what we're going to do this year!

Don't worry—you will not be working alone. Working with others is a skill that you will need throughout your life. When you begin your career, you will most likely work with all sorts of people, from shy to outgoing, from leaders to supporters, from innovators to problem solvers—and many more types of people! Throughout this book, you will have many opportunities to work with your classmates. You will be able to discuss your ideas and predictions to different problem situations; present your calculations and solutions to questions; and analyze, critique and suggest, or support your classmates' answers to problem situations.

Today's workplace demands teamwork and self-confidence. At Carnegie Learning, our goal is to provide you with opportunities to be successful in your math course. Enjoy the year and have fun Learning by Doing™!

—The Carnegie Learning Curriculum Development Team

Acknowledgments

Carnegie Learning Curriculum Development Team

- Michael Amick
  Math Editor
- Joshua Fisher
  Math Editor
- Allison Dockter
  Math Editor
- John Fitsioris
  Curriculum Developer

- Danielle Kandrack
  Math Editor
- Beth Karambelkar
  Curriculum Developer
- David "Augie" Rivera
  Math Editor
- Lezlee Ross
  Curriculum Developer

Vendors

- Cenveo Corporation
- Mathematical Expressions
- Bookmasters, Inc.

- Mind Over Media
- Lapiz
- eInstruction

Special Thanks

- Carnegie Learning Managers of School Partnerships for their content review
- Teacher reviewers and students for their input and review of lesson content
- Carnegie Learning Software Development Team for their contributions to research and content
- Jaclyn Snyder for being a mentor to the development team, her leadership, and her pedagogical pioneering in mathematics education
- Amy Jones Lewis for her review of content
- Colleen Wolfe for project management

Photograph Credits

Chapter 1 © iStockphoto.com/ marekuliasz;

Chapter 2 © iStockphoto.com/ Cristian Baitg;

Chapter 3 © David Rivera/ Aquarium of the Pacific;

Chapter 4 © iStockphoto.com/ Alistair Forrester Shankie;

Chapter 5 © iStockphoto.com/ Steve Maehl;

Chapter 6 © iStockphoto.com/ Carolina K. Smith, M.D.;

Chapter 7 © iStockphoto.com/ Ryan Kelly;

Chapter 8 © iStockphoto.com/ Florin Tirlea;

Acknowledgments

Table of Contents

Searching for Patterns 109

Quadratic Functions 195

Table of Contents

Polynomial Functions 313

Polynomial Expressions and Equations 423

Polynomial Models 511

Sequences and Series 571

Table of Contents

The Crew

The Crew is here to help you throughout the text. Sometimes they will remind you about things you have already learned. Sometimes they will ask you questions to help you think about different strategies. Sometimes they will share fun facts. They are members of your group—someone you can rely on!

Teacher aides will guide you along your way. They will help you make connections and remind you to think about the details.

Introduction

During this course, you will solve problems and work with many different representations of mathematical concepts, ideas, and processes to better understand the world. Each lesson will provide you with opportunities to discuss your ideas, work within groups, and share your solutions and methods with your class. These process icons are placed throughout the text.

Discuss to Understand

- Read the problem carefully.
- What is the context of the problem? Do we understand it?
- What is the question that we are being asked? Does it make sense?
- Is this problem similar to some other problem we know?

Think for Yourself

- Do I need any additional information to answer the question?
- Is this problem similar to some other problem that I know?
- How can I represent the problem using a picture, a diagram, symbols, or some other representation?

Work with Your Partner

- How did you do the problem?
- Show me your representation.
- This is the way I thought about the problem—how did you think about it?
- What else do we need to solve the problem?
- Does our reasoning and our answer make sense to each other?
- How will we explain our solution to the class?

Share with the Class

- Here is our solution and the methods we used.
- Are we communicating our strategies clearly?
- We could only get this far with our solution. How can we finish?
- Could we have used a different strategy to solve the problem?

Representations

Key Terms of the Course

There are important terms you will encounter throughout this book. It is important that you have an understanding of these words as you get started through the mathematical concepts. Knowing what is meant by these terms and using these terms will help you think, reason, and communicate your ideas. The Graphic Organizers shown display a definition for a key term, related words, sample questions, and examples.

You will see these terms throughout each lesson.

Definition

To study or look closely for patterns.

Analyzing can involve examining or breaking a concept down into smaller parts to gain a better understanding of it.

Related Words

- examine
- evaluate
- determine
- observe
- consider
- investigate
- what do you notice?
- what do you think?
- sort and match
- identify

Ask Yourself

- Do I see any patterns?
- Have I seen something like this before?
- What happens if the shape, representation, or numbers change?
- What is the question asking me to accomplish?
- What is the context?
- What does the solution mean in terms of this problem situation?

Analyze

Example

PROBLEM 1   **Feeling a Little Congested**

City planners consider building a new stadium on several acres of land close to the downtown of a large city. They monitored the number of cars entering and exiting downtown from a major highway between 1:00 PM and 7:00 PM to determine current traffic conditions.

1. Analyze the table of values that represent the average number of cars entering and exiting downtown during the given hours of a typical weekday. The value for time represents the start-time for the full hour over which the vehicles were monitored.

Time (PM)	Average Number of Vehicles on a Typical Weekday (thousands)
1:00	7.0
2:00	10.8
3:00	14.5
4:00	21.1
5:00	23.9
6:00	19.0
7:00	10.0

> When entering the data into your calculator, enter 1:00 as 1, 2:00 as 2, 3:00 as 3, etc.

a. Describe any patterns you notice. Explain the patterns in the context of this problem situation.

The number of cars increase, reach a maximum at 5:00 PM, and then decrease again. This pattern makes sense in the context of this problem because rush hour occurs around 5:00 PM.

b. Predict the type of polynomial that best fits the data. Explain your reasoning.

Answers will vary.

The data increases and then decreases. The curve appears to be quadratic.

Definition

To give details or describe how to determine an answer or solution.

Explaining your reasoning helps justify conclusions.

Related Words

- show your work
- explain your calculation
- justify
- why or why not?

Ask Yourself

- How should I organize my thoughts?
- Is my explanation logical?
- Does my reasoning make sense?
- How can I justify my answer to others?
- Did I use complete sentences in my answer?

Don't forget to check your answers!

Explain Your Reasoning

Example

12. Circle the function(s) shown that could describe the given graph. Explain your reasoning.

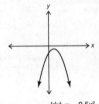

$h(x) = -2x^2 + 3x - 2$

$k(x) = -0.5x^2 + 1.5x + 1$

$t(x) = -\frac{1}{2}x^2 + 3x - \frac{9}{2}$

$w(x) = 2x^2 - 4x - 10$

Only $h(x)$ could describe the function whose graph is shown. The discriminant of $h(x)$ is -7, so it does not intersect the x-axis.

The discriminant of $k(x)$ is 4.25, so it intersects the x-axis twice. Also, $k(x)$ has a positive y-intercept.

The discriminant of $t(x)$ is equal to 0, so it intersects the x-axis one time.

The discriminant of $w(x)$ is 96, so it intersects the x-axis twice. Also, $w(x)$ is concave up.

Definition

To display information in various ways.

Representing mathematics can be done using words, tables, graphs, or symbols.

Related Words

- show
- sketch
- draw
- create
- plot
- graph
- write an equation
- complete the table

Ask Yourself

- How should I organize my thoughts?
- How do I use this model to show a concept or idea?
- What does this representation tell me?
- Is my representation accurate?
- What units or labels should I include?
- Are there other ways to model this concept?

Represent

Example

PROBLEM 4 **Just Another Day at the Circus**

Write a quadratic function to represent each situation using the given information. Be sure to define your variables.

1. The Amazing Larry is a human cannonball. He would like to reach a maximum height of 30 feet during his next launch. Based on Amazing Larry's previous launches, his assistant DaJuan has estimated that this will occur when he is 40 feet from the cannon. When Amazing Larry is shot from the cannon, he is 10 feet above the ground. Write a function to represent Amazing Larry's height in terms of his distance.

Let $h(d)$ represent Amazing Larry's height in terms of his distance, d.

$$h(d) = a(d - 40)^2 + 30$$
$$10 = a(0 - 40)^2 + 30$$
$$10 = 1600a + 30$$
$$-20 = 1600a$$
$$-\frac{1}{80} = a$$

$$h(d) = -\frac{1}{80}(d - 40)^2 + 30$$

Definition

To declare or tell in advance based on the analysis of given data.

Predicting first helps inform reasoning.

Related Words

- estimate
- expect
- approximate
- about how much?

Ask Yourself

- What do I know about this problem situation?
- What predictions can I make from this problem situation?
- Does my reasoning make sense?
- Is my solution close to my estimation?

Predict

Example

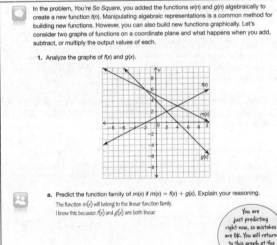

 In the problem, *You're So Square*, you added the functions $w(n)$ and $g(n)$ algebraically to create a new function $t(n)$. Manipulating algebraic representations is a common method for building new functions. However, you can also build new functions graphically. Let's consider two graphs of functions on a coordinate plane and what happens when you add, subtract, or multiply the output values of each.

1. Analyze the graphs of $f(x)$ and $g(x)$.

a. Predict the function family of $m(x)$ if $m(x) = f(x) + g(x)$. Explain your reasoning.

The function $m(x)$ will belong to the linear function family. I know this because $f(x)$ and $g(x)$ are both linear.

b. Predict and sketch the graph of $m(x)$.

See graph.

You are just predicting right now, so mistakes are OK. You will return to this graph at the end of this problem.

c. Explain how you predicted the location of $m(x)$.

Answers will vary.

Definition

To represent or give an account of in words.
Describing communicates mathematical ideas to others.

Related Words

- demonstrate
- label
- display
- compare
- define
- determine
- what are the advantages?
- what are the disadvantages?
- what is similar?
- what is different?

Ask Yourself

- How should I organize my thoughts?
- Is my explanation logical?
- Did I consider the context of this situation?
- Does my reasoning make sense?
- Did I use complete sentences in my answer?
- Did I include appropriate units and labels?
- Will my classmates understand my reasoning?

Describe

Example

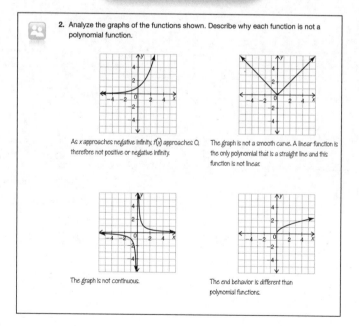

2. Analyze the graphs of the functions shown. Describe why each function is not a polynomial function.

As *x* approaches negative infinity, *f(x)* approaches 0, therefore not positive or negative infinity.

The graph is not a smooth curve. A linear function is the only polynomial that is a straight line and this function is not linear.

The graph is not continuous.

The end behavior is different than polynomial functions.

Problem Types You Will See

Worked Example

WHEN YOU SEE A WORKED EXAMPLE

- Take your time to read through it,
- Question your own understanding, and
- Think about the connections between steps.

ASK YOURSELF

- What is the main idea?
- How would this work if I changed the numbers?
- Have I used these strategies before?

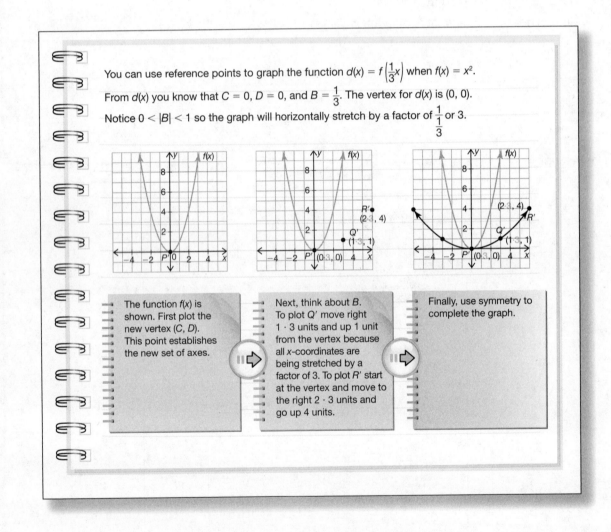

You can use reference points to graph the function $d(x) = f\left(\frac{1}{3}x\right)$ when $f(x) = x^2$.

From $d(x)$ you know that $C = 0$, $D = 0$, and $B = \frac{1}{3}$. The vertex for $d(x)$ is $(0, 0)$.

Notice $0 < |B| < 1$ so the graph will horizontally stretch by a factor of $\frac{1}{\frac{1}{3}}$ or 3.

The function $f(x)$ is shown. First plot the new vertex (C, D). This point establishes the new set of axes.

Next, think about B. To plot Q' move right $1 \cdot 3$ units and up 1 unit from the vertex because all x-coordinates are being stretched by a factor of 3. To plot R' start at the vertex and move to the right $2 \cdot 3$ units and go up 4 units.

Finally, use symmetry to complete the graph.

Thumbs Down

WHEN YOU SEE A THUMBS DOWN ICON

- Take your time to read through the *incorrect* solution.
- Think about what error was made.

ASK YOURSELF

- Where is the error?
- Why is it an error?
- How can I correct it?

5. Emily makes an observation about the number of imaginary zeros a cubic function may have.

 Emily

A cubic function must have three zeros. I know this from the Fundamental Theorem. However, the number of real and imaginary zeros can vary. The function may have 0, 1, 2, or 3 imaginary zeros.

Explain the error in Emily's reasoning.

If a cubic function has imaginary roots, those imaginary roots come from the quadratic function that builds the cubic function. The imaginary roots will appear only in pairs when the quadratic function never intersects the x-axis. Therefore, the number of imaginary zeros a cubic function may have is 0 or 2 imaginary roots.

Problem Types

Thumbs Up

WHEN YOU SEE A THUMBS UP ICON

- Take your time to read through the *correct* solution.
- Think about the connections between steps.

ASK YOURSELF

- Why is this method correct?
- Have I used this method before?

Problem Types

4. Christine and Kate were asked to determine the vertex of two different quadratic functions each written in different forms. Analyze their calculations.

 Christine

$f(x) = 2x^2 + 12x + 10$

The quadratic function is in standard form. So I know the axis of symmetry is $x = \frac{-b}{2a}$.

$$x = \frac{-12}{2(2)}$$

$$= -3.$$

Now that I know the axis of symmetry, I can substitute that value into the function to determine the y-coordinate of the vertex.

$$f(-3) = 2(-3)^2 + 12(-3) + 10$$

$$= 2(9) - 36 + 10$$

$$= 18 - 36 + 10$$

$$= 8$$

Therefore, the vertex is (3, 8).

 Kate

$g(x) = \frac{1}{2}(x + 3)(x - 7)$

The form of the function tells me the x-intercepts are −3 and 7. I also know the x-coordinate of the vertex will be directly in the middle of the x-intercepts. So, all I have to do is calculate the average.

$$x = \frac{-3 + 7}{2}$$

$$= \frac{4}{2} = 2$$

Now that I know the x-coordinate of the vertex, I can substitute that value into the function to determine the y-coordinate.

$$g(2) = \frac{1}{2}(2 + 3)(2 - 7)$$

$$= \frac{1}{2}(5)(-5)$$

$$= -12.5$$

Therefore, the vertex is (2, −12.5).

a. How are these methods similar? How are they different?

Both methods require that you determine the axis of symmetry, and then substitute that value into the function to determine the y-coordinate of the vertex.

The methods are different in the ways the axis of symmetry was determined. Christine used $x = \frac{-b}{2a}$ and Kate used $x = \frac{r_1 + r_2}{2}$.

b. What must Kate do to use Christine's method?

Kate knows the a-value from the form of her quadratic equation. She must multiply the terms together and combine like terms. She would then have a quadratic function in standard form to determine the b-value.

c. What must Christine do to use Kate's method?

Christine must factor the quadratic function or use the quadratic formula to determine the x-intercepts. Once she determines the x-intercepts, she can use the same method as Kate.

Who's Correct?

WHEN YOU SEE A WHO'S CORRECT? ICON

- Take your time to read through the situation.
- Question the strategy or reason given.
- Determine which solution is correct and which is not correct.

ASK YOURSELF

- Does the reasoning make sense?
- If the reasoning makes sense, what is the justification?
- If the reasoning does not make sense, what error was made?

7. Tonya and Alex came up with different expressions to represent the number of gray tiles in each pattern. Their expressions are shown.

Tonya	Alex
$4n^2 + (2n + 1)(2n + 1)$	$(4n + 1)^2 - 4n(2n + 1)$

Tonya claims that they are the same expression written different ways. Alex says, "One expression has addition and the other has subtraction. There is no way they are equivalent!"

Who is correct? Justify your reasoning using algebraic and graphical representations.

Tonya is correct.

Tonya's expression

$4n^2 + (2n + 1)(2n + 1)$

$4n^2 + 4n^2 + 4n + 1$

$8n^2 + 4n + 1$

Alex's expression

$(4n + 1)^2 - 4n(2n + 1)$

$16n^2 + 8n + 1 - 4n^2 - 4n$

$8n^2 + 4n + 1$

Both expressions are equivalent to $8n^2 + 4n + 1$.

When I graph both expressions as equations, they produce the same graph which guarantees equivalence.

The Standards for Mathematical Practice

Effective communication and collaboration are essential skills of a successful learner. With practice, you can develop the habits of mind of a productive mathematical thinker.

Make sense of problems and persevere in solving them.

I can:

- explain what a problem "means" in my own words.
- analyze and organize information.
- keep track of my plan and change it if necessary
- always ask myself, "does this make sense?"

Attend to precision.

I can:

- calculate accurately and efficiently.
- use clear definitions when I talk with my classmates, my teacher, and others.
- specify units of measure and label diagrams and other figures appropriately to clarify the meaning of different representations.

Reasoning and Explaining

Reason abstractly and quantitatively.

I can:

- create an understandable representation of a problem situation.
- consider the units of measure involved in a problem.
- understand and use properties of operations.

Construct viable arguments and critique the reasoning of others.

I can:

- use definitions and previously established results in constructing arguments.
- communicate and defend my own mathematical reasoning using examples, drawings, or diagrams.
- distinguish correct reasoning from reasoning that is flawed.
- listen to or read the conclusions of others and decide whether they make sense.
- ask useful questions in an attempt to understand other ideas and conclusions.

Modeling and Using Tools

Model with mathematics.

I can:

- identify important relationships in a problem situation and represent them using tools such as, diagrams, tables, graphs, and formulas.
- apply mathematics to solve problems that occur in everyday life.
- interpret mathematical results in the contexts of a variety of problem situations.
- reflect on whether my results make sense, improving the model I used if it is not appropriate for the situation.

Use appropriate tools strategically.

I can:

- use a variety of different tools that I have to solve problems.
- use a graphing calculator to explore mathematical concepts.
- recognize when a tool that I have to solve problems might be helpful and also when it has limitations.

Seeing Structure and Generalizing

Look for and make use of structure.

I can:

- look closely to see a pattern or a structure in a mathematical argument.
- can see complicated things as single objects or as being composed of several objects.
- can step back for an overview and can shift my perspective.

Look for and express regularity in repeated reasoning.

I can:

- notice if calculations are repeated.
- look for general methods and more efficient methods to solve problems.
- evaluate the reasonableness of intermediate results.
- make generalizations based on results.

Each lesson provides opportunities for you to think, reason, and communicate mathematical understanding. Here are a few examples of how you will develop expertise using the Standards for Mathematical Practice throughout this text.

PROBLEM 1 Business Is Growing

The Plant-A-Seed Planter Company produces planter boxes. To make the boxes, a square is cut from each corner of a rectangular copper sheet. The sides are bent to form a rectangular prism without a top. Cutting different sized squares from the corners results in different sized planter boxes. Plant-A-Seed takes sales orders from customers who request a sized planter box.

Each rectangular copper sheet is 12 inches by 18 inches. In the diagram, the solid lines indicate where the square corners are cut and the dotted lines represent where the sides are bent for each planter box.

> It may help to create a model of the planter by cutting squares out of the corners of a sheet of paper and folding.

18 inches

12 inches

> **Reason abstractly and quantitatively.**
> You will move from a real-life context to the mathematics and back to the context throughout problems.

1. Organize the information about each sized planter box made from a 12 inch by 18 inch copper sheet.

    a. Complete the table. Include an expression for each planter box's height, width, length, and volume for a square corner side of length h.

> **Model with mathematics.**
> You will identify relationships and represent them using diagrams, tables, graphs, and formulas.

> Recall the volume formula $V = lwh$.

Square Corner Side Length (inches)	Height (inches)	Width (inches)	Length (inches)	Volume (cubic inches)
0				
1				
2				
3				
4				
5				
6				
7				
h				

> **Look for and make use of structure.**
> You will look for patterns in your calculations and use those to write formal expressions and equations.

Habits of Mind

b. What patterns do you notice in the table?

Attend to precision.
You will specify units of measure and express answers with a degree of precision appropriate for the problem context.

2. Analyze the relationship between the height, length, and width of each planter box.

   a. What is the largest sized square corner that can be cut to make a planter box? Explain your reasoning.

   b. What is the relationship between the size of the corner square and the length and width of each planter box?

   c. Write a function $V(h)$ to represent the volume of the planter box in terms of the corner side of length h.

Model with mathematics.
You will identify important quantities and map their relationships using functions.

Construct viable arguments and critique the reasoning of others.
You will share your answers with your classmates and listen to their responses to decide whether they make sense.

Interpreting Data in Normal Distributions

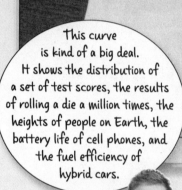

This curve is kind of a big deal. It shows the distribution of a set of test scores, the results of rolling a die a million times, the heights of people on Earth, the battery life of cell phones, and the fuel efficiency of hybrid cars.

Recharge It!
Normal Distributions

Imagine carrying around a cell phone that weighed 80 pounds, provided 30 minutes of talk time on a 100% charged battery, needed 10 hours to fully recharge the battery, and worked in only one assigned local calling area! That's a snapshot of a cell phone in the 1950s.

Cell phones have come a long way since then. Today's cell phone users send and receive texts, emails, photos and videos, they surf the web, play games, use GPS, listen to music, and much more—all on a device that fits in the palm of your hand.

PROBLEM 1 **Low Battery**

Recall that a discrete graph is a graph of isolated points and a continuous graph is a graph of points that are connected by a line or smooth curve on the graph. Data can also be discrete or continuous.

Discrete data are data whose possible values are countable and often finite. The scores of baseball games are examples of discrete data, because a team's score must be a positive whole number or zero.

Continuous data are data which can take any numerical value within a range. Heights of students, times required to complete a test, and distances between cities are examples of continuous data.

Suppose that two cell phone companies, E-Phone and Unlimited, claim that the cell phones of two of their comparable models have a mean battery life of 10 hours.

1. Are the durations of the cell phone batteries examples of discrete data or continuous data? Explain your reasoning.

2. If the mean battery life is 10 hours, does that indicate that all of E-Phone's phones and all of Unlimited's phones have a 10-hour battery life? Explain your reasoning.

One way to display continuous data is by using a relative frequency table. The relative frequency tables shown display the battery lives of a *sample* of 100 E-Phone cell phones and 100 Unlimited cell phones.

A **sample** is a subset of data selected from a *population*. A **population** represents all the possible data that are of interest in a study or survey.

Recall that relative frequency is the ratio of occurrences within an interval to the total number of occurrences.

The battery lives are divided into intervals. Each interval includes the first value but does not include the second value. For example, the interval 8.0–8.5 includes phones with battery lives greater than or equal to 8 hours and less than 8.5 hours.

3. Complete the tables by calculating the relative frequency of phones in each interval. Explain how you determined the relative frequencies.

E-Phone		
Battery Life (hours)	**Number of Phones**	**Relative Frequency**
8.0–8.5	1	
8.5–9.0	2	
9.0–9.5	17	
9.5–10.0	30	
10.0–10.5	32	
10.5–11.0	15	
11.0–11.5	3	
11.5–12.0	0	

Unlimited		
Battery Life (hours)	**Number of Phones**	**Relative Frequency**
8.0–8.5	0	
8.5–9.0	1	
9.0–9.5	14	
9.5–10.0	37	
10.0–10.5	36	
10.5–11.0	11	
11.0–11.5	0	
11.5–12.0	1	

For continuous data, a relative frequency histogram displays continuous intervals on the horizontal axis and relative frequency on the vertical axis.

4. Create a relative frequency histogram to represent the battery lives of the 100 cell phones in each sample.

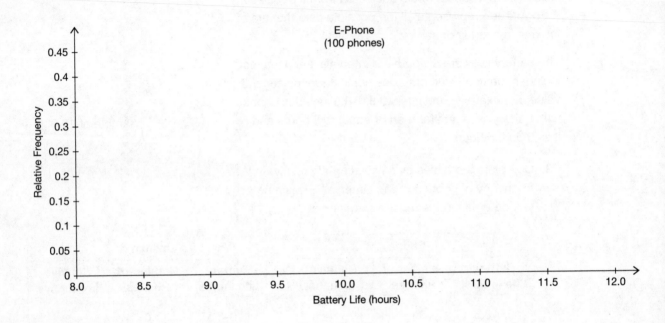

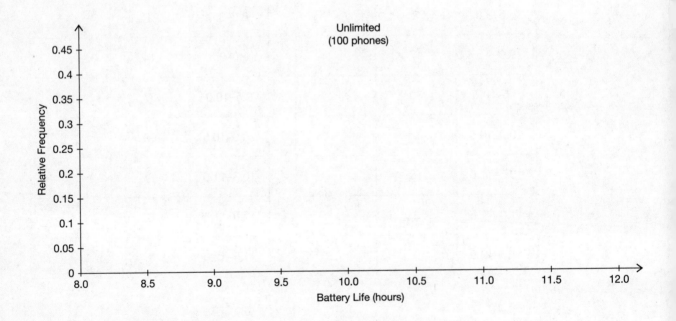

Recall that the shape of a data distribution can reveal information about the data. Data can be widely spread out or packed closer together. Data distributions can also be skewed or symmetric.

5. Describe the shape and spread of the histograms. What might these characteristics reveal about the data for each company?

6. The relative frequency histograms shown represent samples of 10,000 phones from each of the two companies. Compare the histograms created from a sample of 10,000 cell phones to the histograms created from a sample of 100 cell phones. How does increasing the sample size change the appearance of the data distributions?

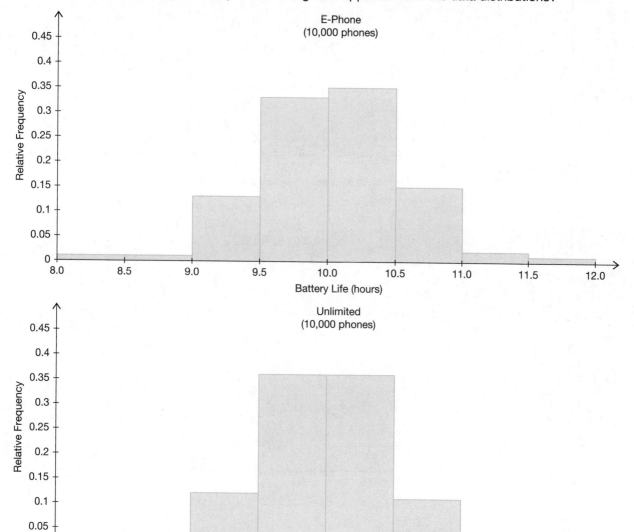

7. The histograms shown represent the same samples of 10,000 phones, but now the data have been divided into intervals of 0.1 hour instead of 0.5 hour. Compare these histograms with the histograms from the previous question. How does decreasing the interval size change the appearance of the data distributions?

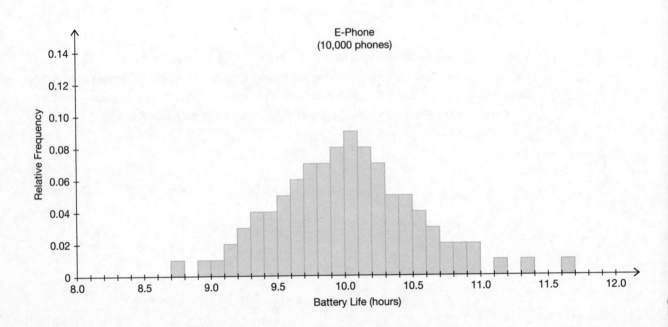

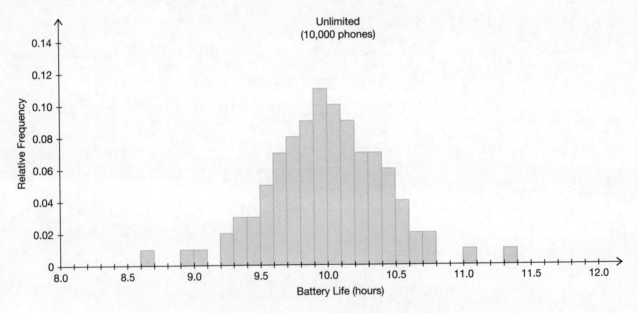

8. Explain why the scale of the *y*-axis changed when the interval size increased.

As the sample size continues to increase and the interval size continues to decrease, the shape of each relative frequency histogram will likely start to resemble a *normal curve*. A **normal curve** is a bell-shaped curve that is symmetric about the mean of the data.

The vertical axis for a graph of a normal curve represents relative frequency, but normal curves are often displayed without a vertical axis.

A normal curve models a theoretical data set that is said to have a **normal distribution**.

The normal curves for the E-Phone and Unlimited cell phone battery lives are shown. In order to display normal curves for each data set, different intervals were used on the horizontal axis in each graph.

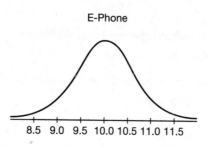

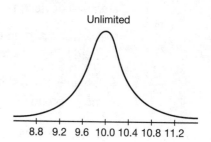

Although normal curves can be narrow or wide, all normal curves are symmetrical about the mean of the data.

Normal Distributions

Not Normal Distributions

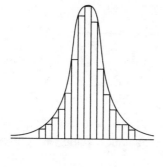

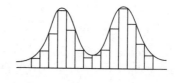

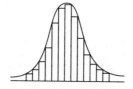

PROBLEM 2 **Deviating Slightly**

You already know a lot about the mean. With normal curves, the **mean** of a population is represented with the symbol μ. The mean of a sample is represented with the symbol $\bar{x}$. The **standard deviation** of data is a measure of how spread out the data are from the mean. The symbol used for the standard deviation of a population is the sigma symbol (σ). The standard deviation of a sample is represented with the variable s. When interpreting the standard deviation of data:

The symbol for mean, μ, is spelled mu and pronounced "myoo."

- A lower standard deviation represents data that are more tightly clustered near the mean.

- A higher standard deviation represents data that are more spread out from the mean.

1. Normal curves *A*, *B*, and *C* represent the battery lives of a population of cell phones of comparable models from three different companies.

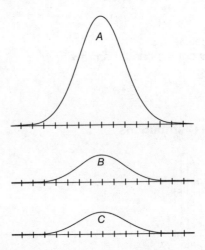

The normal curves represent distributions with standard deviations of σ = 0.1, σ = 0.4, and σ = 0.5. Match each standard deviation value with one of the normal curves and explain your reasoning.

2. Normal curves *A*, *B*, and *C* represent the battery lives of cell phones from three different companies.

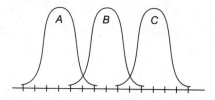

a. Compare the mean of each company.

b. Compare the standard deviation of each distribution.

 Be prepared to share your solutions and methods.

#I'mOnline

The Empirical Rule for Normal Distributions

LEARNING GOALS

In this lesson, you will:

- Recognize the connection between normal curves, relative frequency histograms, and the Empirical Rule for Normal Distributions.
- Use the Empirical Rule for Normal Distributions to determine the percent of data in a given interval.

KEY TERMS

- standard normal distribution
- Empirical Rule for Normal Distributions

On October 19, 1987, stock markets around the world fell into sharp decline. In the United States, the Dow Jones Industrial Average dropped 508 points—a 22% loss in value. Black Monday, as the day came to be called, represented at the time the largest one-day decline in the stock market ever.

According to some economic models, the crash that occurred on Black Monday represented an event that was 20 standard deviations away from the normal behavior of the market. Mathematically, the odds of a Black Monday–type event occurring were 1 in 10^{50}.

PROBLEM 1 Count 'em Up

Let's investigate what the standard deviation can tell us about a normal distribution.

The relative frequency histograms for the battery lives of E-Phone and Unlimited cell phones are shown. The normal curves for each data set are mapped on top of the histogram.

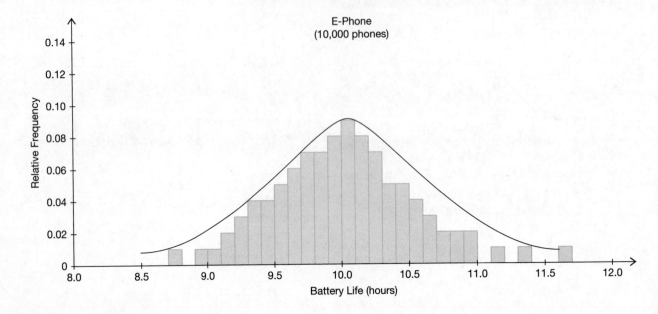

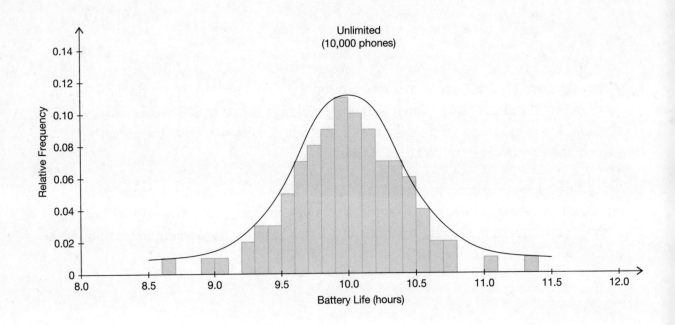

Normal curves can be graphed with units of standard deviation on the horizontal axis. The normal curve for the E-Phone sample has a standard deviation of 0.5 hour ($s = 0.5$), and the normal curve for the Unlimited sample has a standard deviation of 0.4 hour ($s = 0.4$). The mean of each sample is $\bar{x} = 10.0$ hours.

Notice that different symbols are used to represent the mean and standard deviation of a sample as opposed to a population.

1. Study the graphs shown.

   a. For each graph, label each standard deviation unit with its corresponding battery life.

   b. What value is represented at $s = 0$ for both graphs?

2. Use the histograms on the previous page to estimate the percent of data within each standard deviation. Write each percent in the appropriate space below the horizontal axis.

E-Phone

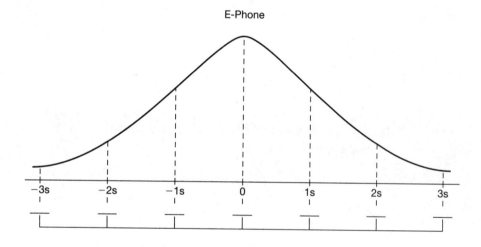

Unlimited

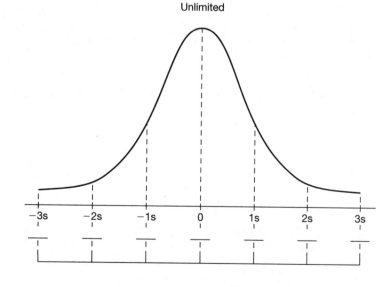

3. Compare the percents in each standard deviation interval for E-Phone with the percents in each standard deviation interval for Unlimited. What do you notice?

4. Use your results to answer each question. Explain your reasoning.

"Within one standard deviation" means between $-1s$ and $1s$, or between -1σ and 1σ.

    a. Estimate the percent of data within 1 standard deviation of the mean.

    b. Estimate the percent of data within 2 standard deviations of the mean.

    c. Estimate the percent of data within 3 standard deviations of the mean.

The **standard normal distribution** is a normal distribution with a mean value of 0 and a standard deviation of 1σ or 1s. In a standard normal distribution, 0 represents the mean. Positive integers represent standard deviations greater than the mean. Negative integers represent standard deviations less than the mean.

> The Empirical Rule for Normal Distributions is often summarized using a standard normal distribution curve because it can be generalized for any normal distribution curve.

The **Empirical Rule for Normal Distributions** states:

* Approximately 68% of the data in a normal distribution for a population is within 1 standard deviation of the mean.

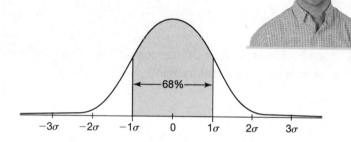

* Approximately 95% of the data in a normal distribution for a population is within 2 standard deviations of the mean.

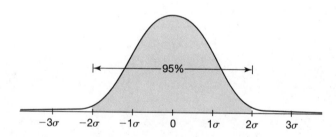

* Approximately 99.7% of the data in a normal distribution for a population is within 3 standard deviations of the mean.

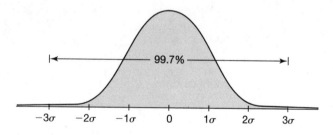

The Empirical Rule applies most accurately to population data rather than sample data. However, the Empirical Rule is often applied to data in large samples.

Recall that a box-and-whisker plot is a graph that organizes, summarizes, and displays data based on quartiles that each contains 25% of the data values.

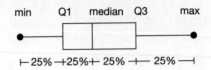

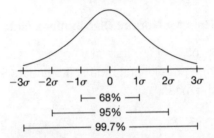

5. What similarities and/or differences do you notice about the box-and-whisker plot and the standard normal distribution?

You can use the Empirical Rule for Normal Distributions to estimate the percent of data within specific intervals of a normal distribution.

1. Determine each percent and explain your reasoning. Shade the corresponding region under each normal curve. Then tell whether the distribution represents population data or sample data.

   a. What percent of the data is greater than the mean?

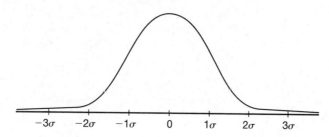

   b. What percent of the data is between the mean and 2 standard deviations below the mean?

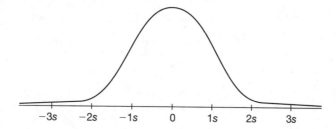

c. What percent of the data is between 1 and 2 standard deviations above the mean?

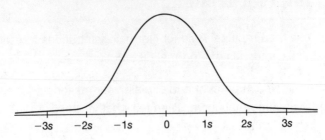

d. What percent of the data is more than 2 standard deviations below the mean?

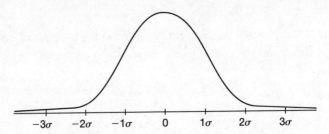

2. Use the normal curve to answer each question and explain your reasoning. Shade the region under each normal curve to represent your answer. Then tell whether the distribution represents population data or sample data.

   a. What percent of adult males have a height between 62 inches and 74 inches?

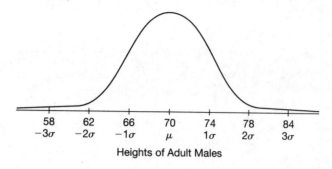

Heights of Adult Males

Keep in mind that 1σ corresponds to a data value that is one standard deviation greater than the population mean and -1σ corresponds to a data value that is one standard deviation less than the mean.

   b. What percent of adult females are taller than 68.5 inches?

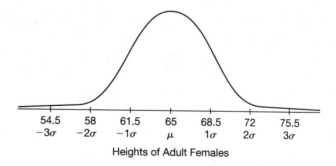

Heights of Adult Females

c. What percent of history test scores are between 63 points and 70 points?

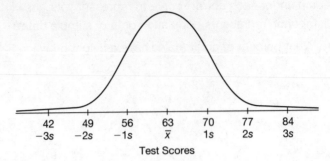

| 42 | 49 | 56 | 63 | 70 | 77 | 84 |
| -3s | -2s | -1s | $\bar{x}$ | 1s | 2s | 3s |

Test Scores

 Be prepared to share your solutions and methods.

Below the Line, Above the Line, and Between the Lines

Z-Scores and Percentiles

LEARNING GOALS

In this lesson, you will:

- Use a z-score table to calculate the percent of data below any given data value, above any given data value, and between any two given data values in a normal distribution.
- Use a graphing calculator to calculate the percent of data below any given data value, above any given data, and between any two given data values in a normal distribution.
- Use a z-score table to determine the data value that represents a given percentile.
- Use a graphing calculator to determine the data value that represents a given percentile.

KEY TERMS

- z-score
- percentile

In 2013, the labels on new vehicles sold in the U.S. got a little different. Instead of just showing how many miles per gallon the vehicle gets, the label also shows the number of gallons per mile it gets.

Why is that important? The reason can be seen on this graph.

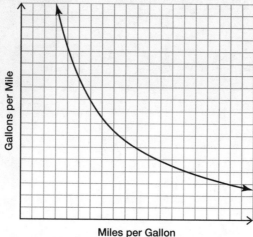

When a car gets a low number of miles per gallon (say, 12 mpg), switching to a slightly higher number (say, 15 mpg) represents a large decrease in the number of gallons per mile, which is a big savings—even bigger than switching from 30 mpg to 50 mpg!

How many gallons per mile does your car get?

PROBLEM 1 **Off the Mark**

1. The fuel efficiency of a sample of hybrid cars is normally distributed with a mean of 54 miles per gallon (mpg) and a standard deviation of 6 miles per gallon.

   So, 1s = 6 mpg.

   a. Use the mean and standard deviation to label the intervals on the horizontal axis of the normal curve in miles per gallon.

   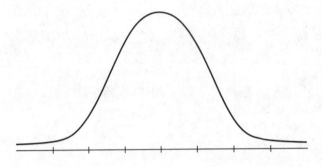

   b. Determine the percent of hybrid cars that get less than 60 miles per gallon. Explain your reasoning.

   c. Determine the percent of hybrid cars that get less than 66 miles per gallon. Explain your reasoning.

   d. Determine the percent of hybrid cars that get less than 72 miles per gallon. Explain your reasoning.

When data values are aligned with integer multiples of the standard deviation from the mean, you can use the Empirical Rule for Normal Distributions to calculate the percent of data values less than that value. But what if a data value does not align with the standard deviations?

2. Let's consider the fuel efficiency of hybrid cars again. The mean is 54 miles per gallon and 1 standard deviation is 6 miles per gallon. What percent of cars get less than 57 miles per gallon?

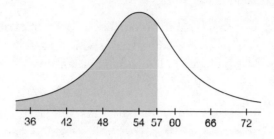

a. How many standard deviations from the mean is 57 miles per gallon? Explain how you determined your answer.

b. Greg incorrectly estimated the percent of hybrid cars that get less than 57 miles per gallon.

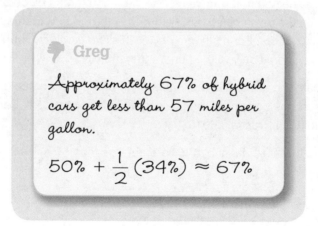

Greg

Approximately 67% of hybrid cars get less than 57 miles per gallon.

$$50\% + \frac{1}{2}(34\%) \approx 67\%$$

Explain why Greg's reasoning is incorrect.

The number you calculated in Question 2 is a *z-score*.
A **z-score** is a number that describes a specific data value's
distance from the mean in terms of standard deviation units.

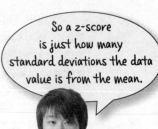

So a z-score
is just how many
standard deviations the data
value is from the mean.

For a population, a z-score is determined by the equation

$$z = \frac{(x - \mu)}{\sigma},$$

where x represents a value from the data.

You can use a z-score table to determine the percent of data
less than a given data value with a corresponding z-score.
A z-score table is provided at the end of this lesson.

To determine the percent of hybrid cars that get less than 57 miles per gallon with a z-score
table, first calculate the z-score for 57 miles per gallon. In Question 2, you calculated the
score for 57 miles per gallon as 0.5.

z	0.0	0.01	0.02	0.03	0.04	0.05
0.0	0.5000	0.5040	0.5080	0.5120	0.5160	0.5199
0.1	0.5398	0.5433	0.5478	0.5517	0.5557	0.5596
0.2	0.5793	0.5832	0.5871	0.5910	0.5948	0.5987
0.3	0.6179	0.6217	0.6255	0.6293	0.6331	0.6368
0.4	0.6554	0.6591	0.6628	0.6664	0.6700	0.6736
0.5	0.6915	0.6950	0.6985	0.7019	0.7054	0.7088

Next, locate the row that represents the ones and tenths place of the z-score. For a z-score
of 0.5, this is the row labeled 0.5. Also locate the column that represents the hundredths
place of the z-score. For a z-score of 0.5, this is the column labeled 0.0. Note that the table
represents z-scores only to the hundredths place.

Finally, locate the cell that is the intersection of the row and column. The numbers in each
cell represent the percent of data values below each z-score. For a z-score of 0.5, the
corresponding cell reads 0.6915.

This means that 69.15% of hybrid cars get less than 57 miles per gallon.

3. What would a negative z-score indicate? Explain your reasoning.

A graphing calculator can determine a percent of data below a z-score. This function is called the normal cumulative density function (normalcdf). The function determines the percent of data values within an interval of a normal distribution.

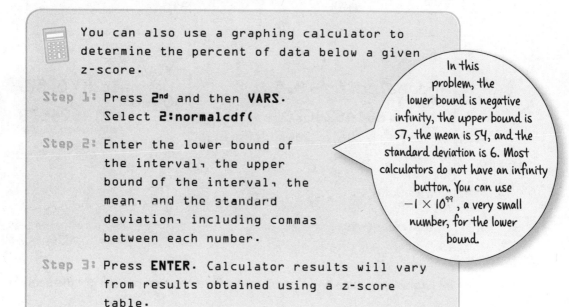

You can also use a graphing calculator to determine the percent of data below a given z-score.

Step 1: Press **2nd** and then **VARS**. Select **2:normalcdf(**

Step 2: Enter the lower bound of the interval, the upper bound of the interval, the mean, and the standard deviation, including commas between each number.

Step 3: Press **ENTER**. Calculator results will vary from results obtained using a z-score table.

In this problem, the lower bound is negative infinity, the upper bound is 57, the mean is 54, and the standard deviation is 6. Most calculators do not have an infinity button. You can use -1×10^{99}, a very small number, for the lower bound.

4. Use a graphing calculator to determine the approximate percent of hybrid cars that get less than 57 miles per gallon.

5. How does this answer compare to the answer you got by using the z-score table?

6. Juan and Michael used a graphing calculator to determine that the percent of hybrid cars that get less than 57 miles per gallon is approximately 69.15%. Juan entered values in standard deviation units, and Michael entered values in terms of miles per gallon.

a. Explain why Juan and Carlos used different values but still got the same result.

b. Explain why Michael used 0 for the lower bound of the interval. Explain why Juan used −9 for the lower bound of the interval.

7. Josh calculated the percent of hybrid cars that get less than 56 miles per gallon using the *z*-score table and a graphing calculator.

z	0.0	0.01	0.02	0.03
0.0	0.5000	0.5040	0.5080	0.5120
0.1	0.5398	0.5438	0.5478	0.5517
0.2	0.5793	0.5832	0.5871	0.5910
0.3	0.6179	0.6217	0.6255	0.6293

> *Josh*
>
> ```
> normalcdf( -1E99,
> 56,54,6)
>            .6305585963
> ```

Explain why Josh received different results from the *z*-score table and the graphing calculator.

PROBLEM **2** **More or Less . . .**

1. Calculate the percent of hybrid cars that get less than 50 miles per gallon.

2. Use your answer to Question 1 to calculate the percent of hybrid cars that get more than 50 miles per gallon. Explain your reasoning.

3. Calculate the percent of hybrid cars that get less than 50 miles per gallon and the percent of hybrid cars that get less than 60 miles per gallon.

4. Use your answer to Question 3 to calculate the percent of hybrid cars that get between 50 and 60 miles per gallon. Explain your reasoning.

PROBLEM 3 **Top Texters**

You may have heard someone say, "My baby's weight is in the 90th percentile" or, "My student scored in the 80th percentile in math." What do these phrases mean?

A **percentile** is a data value for which a certain percentage of the data is below the data value in a normal distribution. For example, 90% of the data in a set is below the value at the 90th percentile, and 80% of the data is below the value at the 80th percentile.

The number of text messages teens send and receive every day can be represented as a normal distribution with a mean of 100 text messages per day and a standard deviation of 25 texts per day.

1. Calculate the 50th percentile for this data set. Explain your reasoning.

2. Would a teen in the 90th percentile send and receive more or fewer than 100 text messages per day? Explain your reasoning.

3. Would a teen in the 10th percentile send and receive more or fewer than 100 text messages per day? Explain your reasoning.

4. Use a z-score table to determine the 90th percentile for teen text messages.

    a. Determine the percent value in the z-score table that is closest to 90%. Explain what information the z-score provides.

    b. Calculate the 90th percentile. Show your work.

You can also use a graphing calculator to calculate a percentile. To calculate a percentile, you can use the inverse of the normal cumulative density function (invNorm). The invNorm function takes a percent as input and returns the data value.

> You can use a graphing calculator to determine the total number of text messages that correspond to the 90th percentile.
>
> Step 1: Press **2nd** and then **VARS**.
>   Select **3:invNorm(**
>
> Step 2: Enter the percentile in decimal form, the mean, and the standard deviation, including commas between each number.
>
> Step 3: Press **ENTER**.

In the texting situation, the percentile is 0.90, the mean is 100, and the standard deviation is 25.

5. Determine the total number of text messages that represent the 20th percentile.

Be prepared to share your solutions and methods.

z-scores and percent of data below the z-score									
z	**0.09**	**0.08**	**0.07**	**0.06**	**0.05**	**0.04**	**0.03**	**0.02**	**0.01**	**0.0**
−3.4	0.0002	0.0003	0.0003	0.0003	0.0003	0.0003	0.0003	0.0003	0.0003	0.0003
−3.3	0.0003	0.0004	0.0004	0.0004	0.0004	0.0004	0.0004	0.0005	0.0005	0.0005
−3.2	0.0005	0.0005	0.0005	0.0006	0.0006	0.0006	0.0006	0.0006	0.0007	0.0007
−3.1	0.0007	0.0007	0.0008	0.0008	0.0008	0.0008	0.0009	0.0009	0.0009	0.0010
−3.0	0.0010	0.0010	0.0011	0.0011	0.0011	0.0012	0.0012	0.0013	0.0013	0.0013
−2.9	0.0014	0.0014	0.0015	0.0015	0.0016	0.0016	0.0017	0.0018	0.0018	0.0019
−2.8	0.0019	0.0020	0.0021	0.0021	0.0022	0.0023	0.0023	0.0024	0.0025	0.0026
−2.7	0.0026	0.0027	0.0028	0.0029	0.0030	0.0031	0.0032	0.0033	0.0034	0.0035
−2.6	0.0036	0.0037	0.0038	0.0039	0.0040	0.0041	0.0043	0.0044	0.0045	0.0047
−2.5	0.0048	0.0049	0.0051	0.0052	0.0054	0.0055	0.0057	0.0059	0.0060	0.0062
−2.4	0.0064	0.0066	0.0068	0.0069	0.0071	0.0073	0.0075	0.0078	0.0080	0.0082
−2.3	0.0084	0.0087	0.0089	0.0091	0.0094	0.0096	0.0099	0.0102	0.0104	0.0107
−2.2	0.0110	0.0113	0.0116	0.0119	0.0122	0.0125	0.0129	0.0132	0.0136	0.0139
−2.1	0.0143	0.0146	0.0150	0.0154	0.0158	0.0162	0.0166	0.0170	0.0174	0.0179
−2.0	0.0183	0.0188	0.0192	0.0197	0.0202	0.0207	0.0212	0.0217	0.0222	0.0228
−1.9	0.0233	0.0239	0.0244	0.0250	0.0256	0.0262	0.0268	0.0274	0.0281	0.0287
−1.8	0.0294	0.0301	0.0307	0.0314	0.0322	0.0329	0.0336	0.0344	0.0351	0.0359
−1.7	0.0367	0.0375	0.0384	0.0392	0.0401	0.0409	0.0418	0.0427	0.0436	0.0446
−1.6	0.0455	0.0465	0.0475	0.0485	0.0495	0.0505	0.0516	0.0526	0.0537	0.0548
−1.5	0.0559	0.0571	0.0582	0.0594	0.0606	0.0618	0.0630	0.0643	0.0655	0.0668
−1.4	0.0681	0.0694	0.0708	0.0721	0.0735	0.0749	0.0764	0.0778	0.0793	0.0808
−1.3	0.0823	0.0838	0.0853	0.0869	0.0885	0.0901	0.0918	0.0934	0.0951	0.0968
−1.2	0.0985	0.1003	0.1020	0.1038	0.1056	0.1075	0.1093	0.1112	0.1131	0.1151
−1.1	0.1170	0.1190	0.1210	0.1230	0.1251	0.1271	0.1292	0.1314	0.1335	0.1357
−1.0	0.1379	0.1401	0.1423	0.1446	0.1469	0.1492	0.1515	0.1539	0.1562	0.1587
−0.9	0.1611	0.1635	0.1660	0.1685	0.1711	0.1736	0.1762	0.1788	0.1814	0.1841
−0.8	0.1867	0.1894	0.1922	0.1949	0.1977	0.2005	0.2033	0.2061	0.2090	0.2119
−0.7	0.2148	0.2177	0.2206	0.2236	0.2266	0.2296	0.2327	0.2358	0.2389	0.2420
−0.6	0.2451	0.2483	0.2514	0.2546	0.2578	0.2611	0.2643	0.2676	0.2709	0.2743
−0.5	0.2776	0.2810	0.2843	0.2877	0.2912	0.2946	0.2981	0.3015	0.3050	0.3085
−0.4	0.3121	0.3156	0.3192	0.3228	0.3264	0.3300	0.3336	0.3372	0.3409	0.3446
−0.3	0.3483	0.3520	0.3557	0.3594	0.3632	0.3669	0.3707	0.3745	0.3783	0.3821
−0.2	0.3829	0.3897	0.3936	0.3974	0.4013	0.4052	0.4090	0.4129	0.4168	0.4207
−0.1	0.4247	0.4286	0.4325	0.4364	0.4404	0.4443	0.4483	0.4522	0.4562	0.4602
−0.0	0.4641	0.4681	0.4721	0.4761	0.4801	0.4840	0.4880	0.4920	0.4960	0.5000

z	0.0	0.01	0.02	0.03	0.04	0.05	0.06	0.07	0.08	0.09
0.0	0.5000	0.5040	0.5080	0.5120	0.5160	0.5199	0.5239	0.5279	0.5319	0.5359
0.1	0.5398	0.5438	0.5478	0.5517	0.5557	0.5596	0.5636	0.5875	0.5714	0.5753
0.2	0.5793	0.5832	0.5871	0.5910	0.5948	0.5967	0.6026	0.6064	0.6103	0.6141
0.3	0.6179	0.6217	0.6255	0.6293	0.6331	0.6368	0.6406	0.6443	0.6480	0.6517
0.4	0.6554	0.6591	0.6628	0.6664	0.6700	0.6736	0.6772	0.6808	0.6844	0.6879
0.5	0.6915	0.6950	0.6985	0.7019	0.7054	0.7068	0.7123	0.7157	0.7190	0.7224
0.6	0.7257	0.7291	0.7324	0.7357	0.7389	0.7422	0.7454	0.7486	0.7517	0.7549
0.7	0.7580	0.7611	0.7642	0.7673	0.7704	0.7734	0.7764	0.7794	0.7823	0.7852
0.8	0.7881	0.7910	0.7939	0.7967	0.7995	0.8023	0.8051	0.8078	0.8106	0.8133
0.9	0.8159	0.8186	0.8212	0.8238	0.8264	0.8269	0.8315	0.8340	0.8365	0.8389
1.0	0.8413	0.8438	0.8461	0.8485	0.8508	0.8531	0.8554	0.8577	0.8599	0.8621
1.1	0.8643	0.8665	0.8686	0.8708	0.8729	0.8749	0.8770	0.8790	0.8810	0.8830
1.2	0.8849	0.8869	0.8888	0.8907	0.8925	0.8944	0.8962	0.8960	0.8997	0.9015
1.3	0.9032	0.9049	0.9066	0.9082	0.9099	0.9115	0.9131	0.9147	0.9162	0.9177
1.4	0.9192	0.9207	0.9222	0.9236	0.9251	0.9265	0.9279	0.9292	0.9306	0.9319
1.5	0.9332	0.9345	0.9357	0.9370	0.9382	0.9394	0.9406	0.9418	0.9429	0.9441
1.6	0.9452	0.9463	0.9474	0.9484	0.9495	0.9505	0.9515	0.9525	0.9535	0.9545
1.7	0.9554	0.9564	0.9573	0.9582	0.9591	0.9599	0.9608	0.9616	0.9625	0.9633
1.8	0.9641	0.9649	0.9656	0.9664	0.9671	0.9678	0.9666	0.9693	0.9699	0.9706
1.9	0.9713	0.9719	0.9726	0.9732	0.9738	0.9744	0.9750	0.9756	0.9761	0.9767
2.0	0.9772	0.9778	0.9783	0.9788	0.9793	0.9798	0.9803	0.9808	0.9812	0.9817
2.1	0.9821	0.9826	0.9830	0.9834	0.9838	0.9842	0.9846	0.9850	0.9854	0.9857
2.2	0.9861	0.9864	0.9868	0.9871	0.9875	0.9878	0.9881	0.9884	0.9887	0.9890
2.3	0.9893	0.9896	0.9898	0.9901	0.9904	0.9906	0.9909	0.9911	0.9913	0.9916
2.4	0.9918	0.9920	0.9922	0.9925	0.9927	0.9929	0.9931	0.9932	0.9934	0.9936
2.5	0.9938	0.9940	0.9941	0.9943	0.9945	0.9946	0.9948	0.9949	0.9951	0.9952
2.6	0.9953	0.9955	0.9956	0.9957	0.9959	0.9960	0.9961	0.9962	0.9963	0.9964
2.7	0.9965	0.9966	0.9967	0.9968	0.9969	0.9970	0.9971	0.9972	0.9973	0.9974
2.8	0.9974	0.9975	0.9976	0.9977	0.9977	0.9978	0.9979	0.9979	0.9980	0.9981
2.9	0.9981	0.9982	0.9982	09983	0.9984	0.9984	0.9985	0.9985	0.9986	0.9986
3.0	0.9987	0.9987	0.9987	0.9988	0.9988	0.9989	0.9989	0.9989	0.9990	0.9990
3.1	0.9990	0.9991	0.9991	0.9991	0.9992	0.9992	0.9992	0.9992	0.9993	0.9993
3.2	0.9993	0.9993	0.9994	0.9994	0.9994	0.9994	0.9994	0.9995	0.9995	0.9995
3.3	0.9995	0.9995	0.9995	0.9996	0.9996	0.9996	0.9996	0.9996	0.9996	0.9997
3.4	0.9997	0.9997	0.9997	0.9997	0.9997	0.9997	0.9997	0.9997	0.9997	0.9998

You Make the Call
Normal Distributions and Probability

In this lesson, you will:

- Interpret a normal curve in terms of probability.
- Use normal distributions to determine probabilities.
- Use normal distributions and probabilities to make decisions.

You can grow both tomatoes and potatoes easily in a home garden—separately—but what about a plant that can grow both vegetables (or is it a fruit and a vegetable?) at the same time?

A company based in the United Kingdom created just that—a hybrid plant that produces both tomatoes above the ground and potatoes below. This remarkable plant was not created through genetic engineering, but rather by grafting the two types of plants together at the stem.

Now for the important question: What would you call this hybrid plant?

So far, you have explored the percent of data values that fall within specified intervals. However, you can also interpret a normal distribution in terms of probabilities.

Based on a survey, the number of text messages that teens send and receive every day is a normal distribution with a mean of 100 text messages per day and a standard deviation of 25 text messages per day.

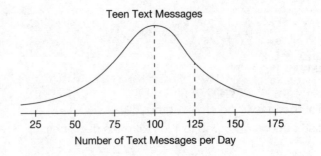

Teen Text Messages

Number of Text Messages per Day

You randomly select a teen from the survey. Calculate each probability.

1. Determine the probability that the randomly selected teen sends and receives between 100 and 125 text messages per day.

2. Determine the probability that the randomly selected teen sends and receives fewer than 75 text messages per day.

3. Determine the probability that the randomly selected teen sends and receives more than 140 text messages per day.

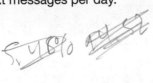

You have collected data on the delivery times for two local pizza shops, Antonio's Pizza and Wood Fire Pizza. Based on your data, Antonio's Pizza has a mean delivery time of 30 minutes and a standard deviation of 3 minutes. Wood Fired Pizza has a mean delivery time of 25 minutes and a standard deviation of 8 minutes.

1. What factors could influence the delivery time of an order from either pizza shop?

Antonios
mean: 30
σ = 3

wood
mean = 25
σ = 8

2. What can you conclude based only on the mean and standard deviation for each pizza shop?

Woods is faster but not consistent
Antonios is slower but consistence

3. A friend of yours is planning a party. She needs the pizza for the party delivered in 35 minutes or less or the party will be a complete disaster! Which pizza shop has a greater probability of delivering the order within 35 minutes?

Antoniols   95.22%
Firewood   89.35%

Antoniols is ~~not~~ better for
being delivered under 35 mint
minuts

PROBLEM 3   **You Say Tomato, I Say Prize-Winning Tomato!**

1. Brad and Toby both plan to enter the county tomato growing competition. Each person who enters the competition must submit a basket of tomatoes. The judges randomly select a tomato from each contestant's basket. According to the rules of the competition, a "golden" tomato has a diameter between 4 inches and 4.5 inches.

The diameters of tomatoes in Brad's basket are normally distributed with a mean diameter of 3.6 inches and a standard deviation of 1 inch. The diameters of tomatoes in Toby's basket are also normally distributed with a mean diameter of 3.8 inches and a standard deviation of 0.2 inches.

When the judges randomly select a tomato from Brad's and Toby's basket, whose is more likely to result in a "golden" tomato?

Be prepared to share your solutions and methods.

Chapter 1 Summary

KEY TERMS

- discrete data (1.1)
- continuous data (1.1)
- sample (1.1)
- population (1.1)
- normal curve (1.1)

- normal distribution (1.1)
- mean (μ) (1.1)
- standard deviation (σ) (1.1)
- standard normal distribution (1.2)

- Empirical Rule for Normal Distributions (1.2)
- z-score (1.3)
- percentile (1.3)

1.1 Differentiating Between Discrete Data and Continuous Data

Discrete data are data whose possible values are countable and often finite. The scores of baseball games are examples of discrete data, because a term's score must be a positive whole number or zero.

Continuous data are data which can take any numerical value within a range. Heights of students, times required to complete a test, and distances between cities are examples of continuous data.

Example

The heights of basketball players are examples of continuous data.

Drawing Distributions for Continuous Data

For continuous data, a relative frequency histogram displays continuous intervals on the horizontal axis and relative frequency on the vertical axis.

Example

Weights of Chicken Eggs (ounces)	Relative Frequency
0.0–0.5	0.05
0.5–1.0	0.23
1.0–1.5	0.44
1.5–2.0	0.22
2.0–2.4	0.06

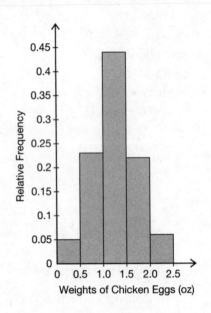

1.1 Recognizing the Difference Between Normal Distributions and Non-normal Distributions

A normal distribution is bell-shaped and symmetrical, and a non-normal distribution is neither bell-shaped nor symmetrical.

Example

The graph does not represent a normal distribution. It is neither bell-shaped nor symmetric, it is skewed.

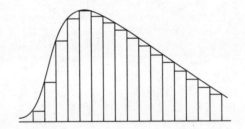

1.1 Recognizing and Interpreting Properties of a Normal Curve and a Normal Distribution

The mean of a normal curve is at the center of the curve. The standard deviation of a normal distribution describes how spread out the data are.

The symbol for the population mean is μ, and the symbol for the sample mean is $\bar{x}$. The standard deviation of a sample is represented with the variable s. The standard deviation of a population is represented with the symbol σ.

Example

The mean is 2.6 and the standard deviation is 0.4.

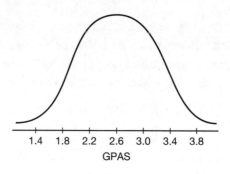

1.2 Recognizing the Connection Between Normal Curves, Relative Frequency Histograms, and the Empirical Rule for Normal Distributions

The standard normal distribution is a normal distribution with a mean value of zero and a standard deviation of 1. The Empirical Rule states that approximately 68% of the data in a normal distribution is within 1 standard deviation of the mean, 95% is within two standard deviations of the mean, and 99.7% is within three standard deviations of the mean.

Example

The percent of data that is more than 2 standard deviations above the mean for the standard normal curve is shaded.

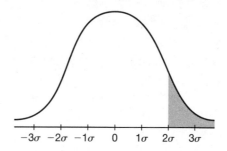

The Empirical Rule for Normal Distributions states that approximately 68% of the data in a normal distribution is within one standard deviation of the mean, 95% is within two standard deviations of the mean, and 99.7% is within three standard deviations of the mean. The percent of data for any normal distribution can be determined using the Empirical Rule.

Example

Determine the percent of commute times less than 36 minutes for a certain city, given that the commute times are normally distributed and the mean commute is 41 minutes with a standard deviation of 2.5 minutes.

A commute time of 36 minutes is 2 standard deviations below the mean. The Empirical Rule for Normal Distributions states that 50% of the data is below the mean and that 47.5% of the data is within 2 standard deviations below the mean. So, 50% − 47.5% or 2.5% of the data is below 2 standard deviations below the mean.

Approximately 2.5% of commute times are less than 36 minutes.

1.3 Using a z-score Table to Calculate the Percent of Data Below any Given Data Value, Above any Given Data Value, and Between any Two Given Data Values in a Normal Distribution

Data points can be converted into z-scores which represent the number of standard deviations the data value is from the mean. It is positive if above the mean and negative if below the mean. A z-score table can then be used to determine the percent of data you are looking for based on the z-scores.

Example

You can calculate the percent of adult men taller than 70 inches, given that adult men's heights are normally distributed and the mean height is 69.3 inches with a standard deviation of 2.8 inches.

$$z = \frac{70 - 69.3}{2.8}$$
$$= \frac{0.7}{2.8}$$
$$= 0.25$$

About 59.87% of adult men are shorter than 70 inches, so 100 − 59.87, or 40.13% of adult men are taller than 70 inches.

1.3 Using a Graphing Calculator to Calculate The Percent of Data Below any Given Data Value, Above any Given Data Value, and Between any Two Given Data Values in a Normal Distribution

To determine the percent of data between two scores on a normal curve, a graphing calculator can be used. The function and its arguments are entered as normalcdf(lower bound of the interval, upper bound of the interval, the mean, the standard deviation).

Example

You can determine the percent of adults with IQ scores between 102 and 132, given that IQ scores are normally distributed and the mean IQ score for adults is a 100 with a standard deviation is 15.

Normalcdf (102, 132, 100, 15)

Approximately 43.05% of adults have IQ scores between 102 and 132.

1.3 Using a Z-score Table to Determine The Data Value That Represents a Given Percentile

A percentile is the data value for which a certain percentage of the data is below the data value in a normal distribution. A z-score can be used to determine the data value. First, the percent value in the table closest to the percentage you are looking for should be found. Then the z-score for the percentile can be found from the table. This can be converted back to the original data value by using the formula for a z-score and solving for the x.

Example

You can determine the 80th percentile for SAT scores, given that SAT scores are normally distributed and the mean is 1500 with a standard deviation of 280.

The percent value in the z-score table that is closest to 80% is 0.7995. The z-score for this percent value is 0.84.

$$0.84 = \frac{x - 1500}{280}$$

$$235.2 = x - 1500$$

$$1735.2 = x$$

The SAT score that represents the 80th percentile is approximately 1735.

Using a Graphing Calculator to Determine The Data Value That Represents a Given Percentile

To determine a percentile on a normal curve, a graphing calculator can be used.
The function and its arguments are entered as invNorm(percentile in decimal form, the mean, the standard deviation).

Example

You can determine the 45th percentile for the length of time of a dance studio's recitals, given that the times are normally distributed and the mean is 145 minutes with a standard deviation of 7 minutes.

Invnorm (0.45, 145, 7) ≈ 144.12

The length of time that represents the 45th percentile is approximately 144.12 minutes.

Interpreting a Normal Curve in Terms of Probability

The percent of data values that fall within specified intervals on a normal distribution can also be interpreted as probabilities.

Example

You can calculate the probability that a randomly selected annual precipitation amount in a city is more than 340 inches, given that the amounts are normally distributed with a mean of 320 inches and a standard deviation of 20 inches.

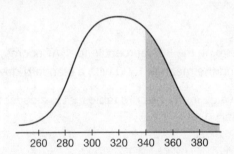

The probability that the randomly selected precipitation amount in a city is more than 340 inches is 16%.

The mean is 320 and one standard deviation above the mean is 340. I know that 34% of the data is between the mean and one standard deviation above the mean. I also know that 50% of the data is above the mean. So, 50 − 34, or 16% of the data is more than one standard deviation above the mean.

1.4 Using Normal Distributions to Determine Probabilities

A normal distribution can be used to determine probabilities. The percent of data between specified intervals represents probabilities. The z-score table or a graphing calculator can be used to find the percents.

Example

You can determine the probability that a randomly selected student will score between a 74 and an 80 on an exam, if the exam scores are normally distributed and the mean is 82 with a standard deviation of 2.8

The probability that a randomly selected student will score between a 74 and an 80 is approximately 23.54%.

Normalcdf(74,80,82,2.8) ≈ 0.2354.

1.4 Using Normal Distributions And Probabilities to Make Decisions

Determining probabilities of events occurring by using percentages from a normal distribution can help to make decisions about different products or situations.

Example

You can determine the factory that should be used to fill an order if it is needed in between 25 and 30 minutes, if Factory A has a mean order time of 27.5 minutes with a standard deviation of 0.8 minutes and Factory B has a mean order time of 28.2 minutes with a standard deviation of 1.2 minutes. Assume both order times can be represented by a normal distribution.

Factory A should be used because it has the best chance of filling an order between 25 and 30 minutes. The probability Factory A will fill the order between 25 and 30 minutes is 99.82%, while the probability that Factory B will fill the order between 25 and 30 minutes is only 92.94%.

Factory A: normalcdf(25, 30, 27.5, 0.8) ≈ 0.9982

Factory B: normalcdf(25, 30, 28.2, 1.2) ≈ 0.9294

Making Inferences and Justifying Conclusions

Every 2, 4, and 6 years, Americans head to the polls to select the women and men who will represent them in the Congress and the White House. And more often than that, these Americans will be polled about their choices. Although election polls can be remarkably accurate, there is always some margin for error.

For Real?

Sample Surveys, Observational Studies, and Experiments

LEARNING GOALS

In this lesson, you will:

- Identify characterlstlcs of sample surveys, observational studies, and experiments.
- Differentiate between sample surveys, observational studies, and experiments.
- Identify possible confounds in the design of experiments.

KEY TERMS

- characteristic of interest
- sample survey
- random sample
- biased sample
- observational study
- experiment
- treatment
- experimental unit
- confounding

Have you taken medicine to treat an illness? Imagine that the medicine you took was not really medicine, but just a sugar pill. In medical studies, people who have unknowingly taken a sugar pill—called a placebo—have reported that the pill has had an effect similar to medicine, even though there was no medicine in the pill at all. This is an example of what is called the placebo effect.

Researchers must always be on the lookout for placebo effects. They may be to blame for successful or unsuccessful outcomes to experiments.

You can use data to help answer questions about the world. The specific question that you are trying to answer or the specific information that you are trying to gather is called a **characteristic of interest**.

For example, you can use data to help determine which drug is most effective, teenagers' favorite television program, or how often doctors wash their hands.

I see how samples are especially useful when collecting data for large populations. Imaging trying to survey every young person in the U.S.!

One way of collecting data is by using a *sample survey*. A **sample survey** poses one or more questions of interest to obtain sample data from a population. Recall, a population represents all the possible data that are of interest in a survey, and a sample is a subset of data that is selected from the population.

A researcher wants to design a sample survey to determine the amount of time that U.S. teenagers between the ages of 16 to 18 spend online each day.

1. Identify the characteristic of interest in the sample survey.

2. Identify the population that the researcher is trying to measure by using a sample survey.

3. Augie and Sandy were discussing the population of the survey.

Augie

The population is all 16- to 18-year-olds in the United States.

Sandy

The population is all teenagers in the United States.

Who is correct? Explain your reasoning.

4. Write a survey question or questions that the researcher could use to collect data from the participants in the survey.

When sample data are collected in order to describe a characteristic of interest, it is important that such a sample be as representative of the population as possible. One way to collect a representative sample is by using a *random sample*. A **random sample** is a sample that is selected from the population in such a way that every member of the population has the same chance of being selected. A **biased sample** is a sample that is collected in a way that makes it unrepresentative of the population.

5. Joanie and Richie were discussing strategies the researcher could use to select a representative sample of 16- to 18-year-olds.

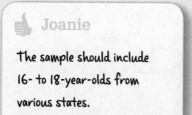

Joanie

The sample should include 16- to 18-year-olds from various states.

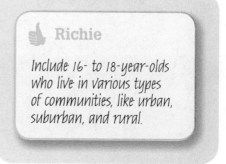

Richie

Include 16- to 18-year-olds who live in various types of communities, like urban, suburban, and rural.

List some additional strategies the researcher should consider when selecting the sample.

6. Cherese suggested that the researcher could post the survey online and then distribute the link to the survey to students after school on Friday as they are leaving the building.

   Will this method result in a biased sample? Explain your reasoning.

Confound It All!

In an **observational study,** data are gathered about a characteristic of the population by simply observing and describing events in their natural settings. Recording the number of children who use the swings at a local park would be an example of a simple observational study.

The results of an observational study state that approximately 70% of in-house day care centers in one U.S. state show as much as 2.5 hours of television to the children per day. The observational study examined 132 day care centers in one state.

1. Identify the population, the sample, and the characteristic of interest in the observational study.

2. List some similarities and differences between an observational study and a sample survey.

An **experiment** gathers data on the effect of one or more **treatments**, or experimental conditions, on the characteristic of interest. Members of a sample, also known as **experimental units**, are randomly assigned to a treatment group.

A placebo treatment is a treatment that is assumed to have no real effect on the characteristic of interest.

Researchers conducted an experiment to test the effectiveness of a new asthma drug. They collected data from a sample of 200 asthma patients. One hundred of the patients received a placebo treatment along with an inhaler. The other one hundred patients received the new drug along with an inhaler. Monthly blood and breathing tests were performed on all 200 patients to determine if the new drug was effective.

3. Identify the population, the sample, and the characteristic of interest in the experiment.

4. What are the treatments in the experiment?

5. What are some ways the researchers could choose a biased sample for this experiment?

Confounding occurs when there are other possible reasons, called confounds, for the results to have occurred that were not identified prior to the study.

6. Suppose one of the treatment groups was given the new drug with an inhaler and the other group was given a placebo with no inhaler. Describe how this design of the experiment introduces a confound.

Talk the Talk

Classify each scenario as a sample survey, an observational study, or an experiment, and explain your reasoning. Then, identify the population, the sample, and the characteristic of interest.

1. To determine whether there is a link between high-voltage power lines and illnesses in children who live in the county, researchers examined the illness rate for 100 children that live within $\frac{1}{4}$ of a mile from power lines and the illness rate for 100 children that live more than $\frac{1}{4}$ of a mile from power lines.

2. Seventy of the school's calculus students are randomly divided into two classes. One class uses a graphing calculator all the time, and the other class never uses graphing calculators. The math department team leader wants to determine whether there is a link between graphing calculator use and students' calculus grades.

3. A medical researcher wants to learn whether or not there is a link between the amount of TV children watch each day and childhood obesity in a particular school district. She gathers data from the records of 15 local pediatricians.

4. In a particular school district, a researcher wants to learn whether or not there is a link between a child's daily amount of physical activity and their overall energy level. During lunch at a school, she distributed a short questionnaire to students in the cafeteria.

Online Time Study, Part I

To design a sample survey, observational study, or experiment, consider these steps:

- Identify the characteristic of interest.

- Identify the population.

- Identify methods to collect the sample so that the sample is not biased.

- Ensure that participants are randomly assigned to a treatment.

- Eliminate elements of the design that may introduce confounding.

1. Design a data collection plan to learn how much time students in your school spend online each day.

   a. Identify the population and the characteristic of interest.

You will revisit this Online Time Study in each lesson of the chapter.

   b. Is the most efficient method for collecting the data a sample survey, an observational study, or an experiment? Explain your reasoning.

   c. Explain how you can gather data from a representative, unbiased sample of students in your school.

Be prepared to share your solutions and methods.

Circle Up
Sampling Methods and Randomization

LEARNING GOALS

In this lesson, you will:

- Use a variety of sampling methods to collect data.
- Identify factors of sampling methods that could contribute to gathering biased data.
- Explore, identify, and interpret the role of randomization in sampling.
- Use data from samples to estimate population mean.

KEY TERMS

- convenience sample
- subjective sample
- volunteer sample
- simple random sample
- stratified random sample
- cluster sample
- cluster
- systematic sample
- parameter
- statistic

What English word is missing below?

_____ _____ _____ _____ _____ _____

When you play word games like this, where you guess the letters until you figure out the word, you think about samples and populations.

For example, you know that the missing word is a sample of the population of words in the English language. Since "e" is a frequently used letter and "z" is used infrequently in words, you would probably guess "e" before you guessed "z".

It is useful in statistics, too, to assume that the characteristics of a sample match those of a population—as long as that sample is chosen wisely!

When you use statistics, you are often measuring the values of a population by focusing on the measurements of a sample of that population. A population does not have to refer to people. It can be any complete group of data—like the areas of 100 circles.

The end of this lesson includes 100 circles and a table. The table lists an identification number, the diameter, and the area for each circle. Suppose you want to determine the mean area of all 100 circles. Calculating the areas of all of the circles would be time-consuming. Instead, you can use different samples of this population of circles to estimate the mean area of the entire population.

1. Without looking at the circles, Mauricia decided to use Circles 1–5 for her sample. Is it likely that those 5 circle areas are representative of all 100 circles? Explain your reasoning.

2. Analyze the circles. Select a sample of 5 circles that you think best represents the entire set of circles.

The sample of circles Mauricia chose is called a *convenience sample*. A **convenience sample** is a sample whose data is based on what is convenient for the person choosing the sample.

The sample of circles you chose in Question 2 is called a *subjective sample*. A **subjective sample** is a sample drawn by making a judgment about which data items to select.

Another type of sample is a *volunteer sample*. A **volunteer sample** is a sample whose data consists of those who volunteer to be part of a sample.

Okay, circles can't really volunteer to be in a sample. But people can!

3. Olivia and Ricky discussed whether a convenience sample or a subjective sample is more likely to be representative of the population of circle areas.

> **Olivia**
>
> I think a subjective sample is more likely to be representative of the 100 circles than the convenience sample.

> **Ricky**
>
> The subjective sample and the convenience sample are equally likely to be representative of the 100 circles.

Who is correct? Explain your reasoning.

4. Olivia shared her conclusion about convenience samples, subjective samples, and volunteer samples.

 Olivia

Even though one method may be better than another in a specific situation, collecting data using a convenience sample, subjective sample, or volunteer sample will likely result in a biased sample.

It's the sampling method that leads to the bias. It's not that an individual sample is biased or not.

Explain why Olivia's statement is correct.

PROBLEM 2   Equal Opportunity for All

A **simple random sample** is a sample composed of data elements that were equally likely to have been chosen from the population.

1. Explain how convenience samples, subjective samples, and volunteer samples do not include data elements that were equally likely to have been chosen from the population.

Using a random digit table is one option for selecting a simple random sample. To use the table, begin at any digit and follow the numbers in a systematic way, such as moving across a row until it ends and then moving to the beginning of the next row.

Random Digit Table									
Line 1	65285	97198	12138	53010	94601	15838	16805	61004	43516	17020
Line 2	17264	57327	38224	29301	31381	38109	34976	65692	98566	29550
Line 3	95639	99754	31199	92558	68368	04985	51092	37780	40261	14479
Line 4	61555	76404	86210	11808	12841	45147	97438	60022	12645	62000
Line 5	78137	98768	04689	87130	79225	08153	84967	64539	79493	74917
Line 6	62490	99215	84987	28759	19177	14733	24550	28067	68894	38490
Line 7	24216	63444	21283	07044	92729	37284	13211	37485	10415	36457
Line 8	16975	95428	33226	55903	31605	43817	22250	03918	46999	98501
Line 9	59138	39542	71168	57609	91510	77904	74244	50940	31553	62562
Line 10	29478	59652	50414	31966	87912	87154	12944	49862	96566	48825
Line 11	96155	95009	27429	72918	08457	78134	48407	26061	58754	05326
Line 12	29621	66583	62966	12468	20245	14015	04014	35713	03980	03024
Line 13	12639	75291	71020	17265	41598	64074	64629	63293	53307	48766
Line 14	14544	37134	54714	02401	63228	26831	19386	15457	17999	18306
Line 15	83403	88827	09834	11333	68431	31706	26652	04711	34593	22561
Line 16	67642	05204	30697	44806	96989	68403	85621	45556	35434	09532
Line 17	64041	99011	14610	40273	09482	62864	01573	82274	81446	32477
Line 18	17048	94523	97444	59904	16936	39384	97551	09620	63932	03091
Line 19	93039	89416	52795	10631	09728	68202	20963	02477	55494	39563
Line 20	82244	34392	96607	17220	51984	10753	76272	50985	97593	34320

You can use two digits at a time to choose a sample of 5 circles.

2. Select a simple random sample of 5 circles using the random digit table. Pick any row of the table. Use the first two digits to represent the first circle of the sample, the next two digits to represent the second circle of the sample, and so on. List the identification numbers of the 5 circles.

If the same two-digit number comes up more than once, I'll skip it each time it is repeated and go to the next number.

You can also use a graphing calculator to generate a random list of numbers.

> You can use a graphing calculator to generate a random list of numbers and select a simple random sample of 5 circles.
>
> Step 1: Press **MATH**.
> Scroll to the **PRB** menu.
> Select **5:randInt(**
>
> Step 2: Enter a lower bound for the random number, an upper bound for the random number, and how many random numbers to generate. Use commas between values as you enter them.
>
> Step 3: Press **ENTER**.

The lower bound is 0, the upper bound is 99, and the number of random numbers to generate is 5.

3. Use a graphing calculator to generate a random sample of 5 circles.

4. Calculate the mean area of the circles in your simple random sample.

5. Compare your simple random sample with your classmates' samples. What do you notice?

There are several other types of random samples, including *stratified random samples, cluster samples*, and *systematic samples*.

A **stratified random sample** is a random sample obtained by dividing a population into different groups, or strata, according to a characteristic and randomly selecting data from each group.

You can collect a stratified random sample of circles by first dividing the circles into groups.

Define groups of circles based on the lengths of their diameters.

- Small circles: diameter $\leq \frac{1}{4}$ in.
- Medium circles: $\frac{1}{4}$ in. $<$ diameter $\leq 1\frac{1}{2}$ in.
- Large circles: diameter $> 1\frac{1}{2}$ in.

Small Circles (46)	Medium Circles (39)	Large Circles (15)
1, 4, 6, 13, 14, 16, 17, 19, 22, 24, 26, 28, 30, 33, 34, 37, 39, 42, 45, 46, 47, 51, 53, 56, 57, 58, 59, 62, 63, 67, 68, 72, 74, 78, 79, 82, 85, 87, 88, 89, 93, 94, 95, 97, 98, 99	0, 2, 3, 8, 9, 10, 11, 12, 21, 23, 25, 29, 31, 35, 36, 40, 41, 43, 49, 50, 52, 61, 64, 65, 66, 69, 71, 73, 75, 76, 77, 80, 81, 83, 84, 86, 90, 91, 96	5, 7, 15, 18, 20, 27, 32, 38, 44, 48, 54, 55, 60, 70, 92

There are about an equal number of small and medium circles and about a third as many small circles. To maintain this ratio in your stratified random sample, you can choose 3 small circles, 3 medium circles, and 1 small circle.

Select random circles from each group using a random digit table or a graphing calculator.

> Another option is to randomly select 2 large circles, 6 medium circles, and 6 small circles. This keeps the ratios the same.

6. Collect a stratified random sample of circles. List the sample and explain your method.

7. Calculate the mean of the circle areas in your stratified random sample.

A **cluster sample** is a random sample that is obtained by creating *clusters*. Then, one cluster is randomly selected for the sample. Each **cluster** contains the characteristics of a population.

8. Use the page that contains the circles at the end of this lesson to answer each question.

   a. Draw 4 horizontal lines and 2 vertical lines so that the page is divided into 12 congruent rectangles. Each rectangle represents a cluster of circles. Number each cluster from 1 to 12.

Here we have to assume that each rectangle contains a representative cluster of circles.

   b. Use a graphing calculator or the random digit table to randomly select one of the clusters. List the cluster sample.

   c. Calculate the mean of the circle areas included in your cluster sample.

A **systematic sample** is a random sample obtained by selecting every *n*th data value in a population.

9. Select a systematic sample by choosing every 20th circle. First, randomly choose a number from 0 to 20 to start at and then choose every 20th circle after that.

10. Calculate the mean of the circle areas included in your systematic sample.

11. Faheem and Calvin shared their thoughts about random sampling.

Faheem

Simple random sampling, stratified random sampling, and cluster sampling will always produce a representative, unbiased sample.

Calvin

Simple random sampling, stratified random sampling, or cluster sampling does not guarantee a representative, unbiased sample.

Who is correct? Explain your reasoning.

The mean of a sample, $\bar{x}$, can be used to estimate the population mean, μ. The population mean is an example of a **parameter**, because it is a value that refers to a population. The sample mean is an example of a **statistic**, because it is a value that refers to a sample.

The population mean for the 100 circles is $\mu = 0.58\pi$ square inches, or approximately 1.82 square inches.

12. Carla collected three simple random samples from the population of 100 circles and calculated the mean of each sample.

> Carla
>
> I didn't expect the sample of 5 circles to have a mean closest to the mean of the population. I must have done something wrong when collecting the samples.
>
> Mean of 5 circles $\approx 0.55\pi$ square inches
>
> Mean of 15 circles $\approx 0.49\pi$ square inches
>
> Mean of 30 circles $\approx 0.65\pi$ square inches

Is Carla's statement correct? Explain your reasoning.

Online Time Study, Part II

In the first lesson of this chapter, you designed a plan to learn about the amount of time students in your school are online each day.

1. Which sampling method would be best to select the data? Explain your reasoning.

How can you apply your new knowledge of sampling to the Online Time Study?

Be prepared to share your results and methods.

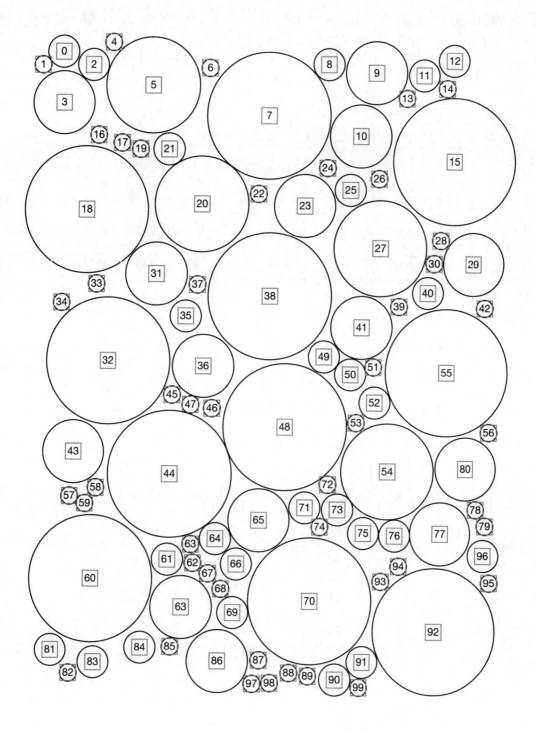

Circle Number	Diameter (in.)	Area (in.²)	Circle Number	Diameter (in.)	Area (in.²)	Circle Number	Diameter (in.)	Area (in.²)
0	$\frac{1}{2}$	$\frac{1}{16}\pi$	18	2	π	36	1	$\frac{1}{4}\pi$
1	$\frac{1}{4}$	$\frac{1}{64}\pi$	19	$\frac{1}{4}$	$\frac{1}{64}\pi$	37	$\frac{1}{4}$	$\frac{1}{64}\pi$
2	$\frac{1}{2}$	$\frac{1}{16}\pi$	20	$1\frac{1}{2}$	$\frac{9}{16}\pi$	38	2	π
3	1	$\frac{1}{4}\pi$	21	$\frac{1}{2}$	$\frac{1}{16}\pi$	39	$\frac{1}{4}$	$\frac{1}{64}\pi$
4	$\frac{1}{4}$	$\frac{1}{64}\pi$	22	$\frac{1}{4}$	$\frac{1}{64}\pi$	40	$\frac{1}{2}$	$\frac{1}{16}\pi$
5	$1\frac{1}{2}$	$\frac{9}{16}\pi$	23	1	$\frac{1}{4}\pi$	41	1	$\frac{1}{4}\pi$
6	$\frac{1}{4}$	$\frac{1}{64}\pi$	24	$\frac{1}{4}$	$\frac{1}{64}\pi$	42	$\frac{1}{4}$	$\frac{1}{64}\pi$
7	2	π	25	$\frac{1}{2}$	$\frac{1}{4}\pi$	43	1	$\frac{1}{4}\pi$
8	$\frac{1}{2}$	$\frac{1}{16}\pi$	26	$\frac{1}{4}$	$\frac{1}{64}\pi$	44	2	π
9	1	$\frac{1}{4}\pi$	27	$1\frac{1}{2}$	$\frac{9}{16}\pi$	45	$\frac{1}{4}$	$\frac{1}{64}\pi$
10	1	$\frac{1}{4}\pi$	28	$\frac{1}{4}$	$\frac{1}{64}\pi$	46	$\frac{1}{4}$	$\frac{1}{64}\pi$
11	$\frac{1}{2}$	$\frac{1}{16}\pi$	29	1	$\frac{1}{4}\pi$	47	$\frac{1}{4}$	$\frac{1}{64}\pi$
12	$\frac{1}{2}$	$\frac{1}{16}\pi$	30	$\frac{1}{4}$	$\frac{1}{64}\pi$	48	2	π
13	$\frac{1}{4}$	$\frac{1}{64}\pi$	31	1	$\frac{1}{4}\pi$	49	$\frac{1}{2}$	$\frac{1}{16}\pi$
14	$\frac{1}{4}$	$\frac{1}{64}\pi$	32	2	π	50	$\frac{1}{2}$	$\frac{1}{16}\pi$
15	2	π	33	$\frac{1}{4}$	$\frac{1}{64}\pi$	51	$\frac{1}{4}$	$\frac{1}{64}\pi$
16	$\frac{1}{4}$	$\frac{1}{64}\pi$	34	$\frac{1}{4}$	$\frac{1}{64}\pi$	52	$\frac{1}{2}$	$\frac{1}{64}\pi$
17	$\frac{1}{4}$	$\frac{1}{64}\pi$	35	$\frac{1}{2}$	$\frac{1}{16}\pi$	53	$\frac{1}{4}$	$\frac{1}{64}\pi$

Circle Number	Diameter (in.)	Area (in.²)	Circle Number	Diameter (in.)	Area (in.²)	Circle Number	Diameter (in.)	Area (in.²)
54	$1\frac{1}{2}$	$\frac{9}{16}\pi$	72	$\frac{1}{4}$	$\frac{1}{64}\pi$	90	$\frac{1}{2}$	$\frac{1}{16}\pi$
55	2	π	73	$\frac{1}{2}$	$\frac{1}{16}\pi$	91	$\frac{1}{2}$	$\frac{1}{16}\pi$
56	$\frac{1}{4}$	$\frac{1}{64}\pi$	74	$\frac{1}{4}$	$\frac{1}{64}\pi$	92	2	π
57	$\frac{1}{4}$	$\frac{1}{64}\pi$	75	$\frac{1}{2}$	$\frac{1}{16}\pi$	93	$\frac{1}{4}$	$\frac{1}{64}\pi$
58	$\frac{1}{4}$	$\frac{1}{64}\pi$	76	$\frac{1}{2}$	$\frac{1}{16}\pi$	94	$\frac{1}{4}$	$\frac{1}{64}\pi$
59	$\frac{1}{4}$	$\frac{1}{64}\pi$	77	1	$\frac{1}{4}\pi$	95	$\frac{1}{4}$	$\frac{1}{64}\pi$
60	2	π	78	$\frac{1}{4}$	$\frac{1}{64}\pi$	96	$\frac{1}{2}$	$\frac{1}{16}\pi$
61	$\frac{1}{2}$	$\frac{1}{16}\pi$	79	$\frac{1}{4}$	$\frac{1}{64}\pi$	97	$\frac{1}{4}$	$\frac{1}{64}\pi$
62	$\frac{1}{4}$	$\frac{1}{64}\pi$	80	1	$\frac{1}{4}\pi$	98	$\frac{1}{4}$	$\frac{1}{64}\pi$
63	$\frac{1}{4}$	$\frac{1}{64}\pi$	81	$\frac{1}{2}$	$\frac{1}{16}\pi$	99	$\frac{1}{4}$	$\frac{1}{64}\pi$
64	$\frac{1}{2}$	$\frac{1}{16}\pi$	82	$\frac{1}{4}$	$\frac{1}{64}\pi$			
65	1	$\frac{1}{4}\pi$	83	$\frac{1}{2}$	$\frac{1}{16}\pi$			
66	$\frac{1}{2}$	$\frac{1}{16}\pi$	84	$\frac{1}{2}$	$\frac{1}{16}\pi$			
67	$\frac{1}{4}$	$\frac{1}{64}\pi$	85	$\frac{1}{4}$	$\frac{1}{64}\pi$			
68	$\frac{1}{4}$	$\frac{1}{64}\pi$	86	1	$\frac{1}{4}\pi$			
69	$\frac{1}{2}$	$\frac{1}{16}\pi$	87	$\frac{1}{4}$	$\frac{1}{64}\pi$			
70	2	π	88	$\frac{1}{4}$	$\frac{1}{64}\pi$			
71	$\frac{1}{2}$	$\frac{1}{16}\pi$	89	$\frac{1}{4}$	$\frac{1}{64}\pi$			

Sleep Tight

Using Confidence Intervals to Estimate Unknown Population Means

LEARNING GOALS

In this lesson, you will:

- Interpret the margin of error for estimating a population proportion.
- Interpret the margin of error for estimating a population mean.
- Recognize the difference between a sample and a sampling distribution.
- Recognize that data from samples are used to estimate population proportions and population means.
- Use confidence intervals to determine the margin of error of a population proportion estimate.
- Use confidence intervals to determine the margin of error of a population mean estimate.

KEY TERMS

- population proportion
- sample proportion
- sampling distribution
- confidence interval

Why do we have dreams? Scientists still don't really have the answer to that question, but there have been many theories.

Some suggest that dreaming is the brain's way of discarding memories you have gathered during the day but no longer need, and studies have shown that dreaming increases as a result of learning. Another theory suggests that your brain is simply constantly churning out thoughts and images and that this doesn't stop when the rest of your body is asleep.

Some scientists are looking to evolution to provide some clues about why we dream—especially since humans don't seem to be the only animals that dream.

Why do you think some animals dream?

In a poll of 1100 registered voters before an upcoming mayoral election, 594 people, or 54%, said they would vote to re-elect the current mayor, while the remaining voters said they would not vote for the mayor. The margin of error for the poll was ±3 percent, which means that the poll predicts that somewhere between 51% (54% − 3%) and 57% (54% + 3%) of people will actually vote to re-elect the mayor.

> The poll results are categorical data because there are two categories: those who will vote for the mayor and those who won't.

 1. Does the poll represent a sample survey, an observational study, or an experiment?

2. Based on the poll, can you conclude that the current mayor will be re-elected? Explain your reasoning.

 3. Is it possible for fewer than 50% of respondents in a new sample to respond that they will vote for the mayor in the election? Is it likely? Explain your reasoning.

4. With your classmates, conduct a simulation to represent polling a new sample of 1100 voters.

   a. Divide 1100 by the number of students in your class to determine the size of each student's sample.

   b. Generate an amount of random numbers equal to the sample size in part (a) to represent responses to the polling question. Generate random numbers between 1 and 100, with numbers from 1 to 54 representing support for re-electing the mayor and the numbers 55 to 100 representing support for not re-electing the mayor. Tally the results of your simulation, and then list the total number of tallies for each category.

Here we assume that an average of 54% will vote to re-elect the mayor.

Number of People Who Respond that They Will Vote to Re-elect the Mayor	Number of People Who Respond that They Will Not Vote to Re-elect the Mayor

c. Calculate the percent of people who state that they will vote to re-elect the mayor and the percent of people who state that they will vote to not re-elect the mayor based on your simulation.

d. Complete the simulation for the 1100 voters by combining the data from your classmates. List the percent of votes for each category.

Percent of People Who Respond that They Will Vote to Re-elect the Mayor	Percent of People Who Respond that They Will Vote to Not Re-elect the Mayor

e. Are the results of the simulation different from the results of the original poll? Explain.

f. If you conducted the simulation over and over, would you expect to get the same results or different results each time? Explain your reasoning.

The percent of voters who actually vote for the mayor in the election is the **population proportion**. The percent of voters in the sample who respond that they will vote for the mayor is the **sample proportion**. The population proportion and sample proportion are measures used for discrete, or categorical, data. For continuous data, these are called the population mean and sample mean.

For continuous data, it's called the population or sample mean. For categorical data, it's called the population or sample proportion.

When you and your classmates generated random numbers to simulate multiple samples of the 1100 voters, you came up with different sample proportions. The set of all of your classmates' sample proportions is part of a *sampling distribution*.

A **sampling distribution** is the set of sample proportions for all possible equal-sized samples. A sampling distribution will be close to a normal distribution, and the center of a sampling distribution is a good estimate of a population proportion—in this case, the percent of people who will actually vote to re-elect the mayor.

But rather than collecting a very large number of samples, a more practical method for estimating a population proportion is to use the sample proportion of a single sample to estimate the standard deviation of the sampling distribution. The standard deviation of a sampling distribution can give you a range in which the population proportion is likely to fall, relative to the sample proportion.

You can learn the details of deriving the formula for the standard deviation of the sampling distribution, $\sqrt{\dfrac{\hat{p}(1-\hat{p})}{n}}$, in a statistics course.

For example, to estimate the standard deviation of the sampling distribution for the sample of 1100 voters, you can use the formula $\sqrt{\dfrac{\hat{p}(1-\hat{p})}{n}}$, where ($\hat{p}$) is the sample proportion and n is the sample size.

The sample proportion from the original poll is 54%, or 0.54. This is the percent of the 1100 people in the poll who said they would vote to re-elect the mayor.

The standard deviation of the sampling distribution for this poll is

$$\sqrt{\frac{\hat{p}(1-\hat{p})}{n}} = \sqrt{\frac{0.54(1-0.54)}{1100}}$$
$$\approx 0.0150$$

This means that 1 standard deviation below the sample proportion of 54% is 54% − 1.5%, or 52.5%. And 1 standard deviation above the sample proportion of 54% is 54% + 1.5%, or 55.5%.

5. Use the sample proportion and standard deviation of the sampling distribution to label the horizontal axis of the normal curve.

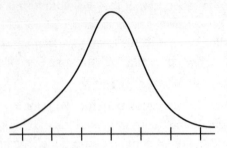

Percent Voting for Mayor's Re-election

6. Bobbie made an observation about the standard deviation of a sampling distribution.

> Bobbie
>
> The standard deviation of a sampling distribution gets smaller and smaller as the size of the sample gets larger and larger.

Is Bobbie's statement correct? Explain why or why not.

An estimated range of values that will likely include the population proportion or population mean is called a **confidence interval**. When stating the margin of error, a 95% confidence interval is typically used. However, other confidence intervals may also be used.

For example, the standard deviation of the sampling distribution for the election sample is 0.015, or 1.5%. Two standard deviations is 3%, so the margin of error is reported as ±3%.

Confidence intervals for a population proportion are calculated using the sample proportion of a sample and the standard deviation of the sampling distribution.

- The lower bound of a 68% confidence interval ranges from 1 standard deviation below the sample proportion to 1 standard deviation above the sample proportion.

- The lower bound of a 95% confidence interval ranges from 2 standard deviations below the sample proportion to 2 standard deviations above the sample proportion.

- The lower bound of a 99.7% confidence interval ranges from 3 standard deviations below the sample proportion to 3 standard deviations above the sample proportion.

7. Determine each confidence interval for the election poll.

 a. 68%

 b. 95%

 c. 99.7%

8. Explain the similarities and differences between each confidence interval for the election poll.

9. The result of the original poll was 54% with 3% margin of error. What confidence interval does 3% represent? Explain your reasoning.

10. Use a 95% confidence interval to determine a margin of error and a range of values for each population proportion.

a. A survey of 1500 teenagers shows that 83% do not like waking up early in the morning.

b. A survey of 200 licensed high school students shows that 16% own their own car.

c. A survey of 500 high school students shows that 90% say math is their favorite class.

A sample of 50 students at High Marks High School responded to a survey about their amount of sleep during an average night. The sample mean was 7.7 hours and the sample standard deviation was 0.8 hour.

Let's determine an estimate for the population mean sleep time for all High Marks High School students.

Notice that 'sample mean' is used instead of 'sample proportion.' This is because the data are continuous.

1. If you gathered data from many new samples, would you expect the samples to have equal means or different means? Explain your reasoning.

Collecting additional samples of 50 students and plotting the sample mean of each sample will result in a sampling distribution. The sampling distribution will be approximately normal, and the mean of the sampling distribution is a good estimate of the population mean.

Just like with the categorical data, a more practical method for estimating the population mean amount of sleep for High Marks High School students is to use the sample mean to calculate an estimate for the standard deviation of the sampling distribution. The formula for the standard deviation of a sampling distribution for continuous data is $\frac{s}{\sqrt{n}}$, where s is the standard deviation of the original sample and n is the sample size.

2. Use the standard deviation from the original sample to determine the standard deviation for the sampling distribution. Explain your work.

Recall that the formula for the standard deviation of a sampling distribution of categorical data is

$$\sqrt{\frac{\hat{p}(1 - \hat{p})}{n}}.$$

3. Use the standard deviation of the sampling distribution to determine a 95% confidence interval for the population mean. Explain your work.

4. Write the 95% confidence interval in terms of the population mean plus or minus a margin of error.

5. Use a 95% confidence interval to determine a range of values for each population mean.

    a. A sample of 75 students responded to a survey about the amount of time spent online each day. The sample mean was 3.2 hours, and the standard deviation of the sampling distribution was 0.9 hour.

    b. A sample of 1000 teachers responded to a survey about the amount of time they spend preparing for class outside of school hours. The sample mean was 2.5 hours, and the standard deviation of the sampling distribution was 0.5 hour.

    c. A sample of 400 adults responded to a survey about the distance from their home to work. The sample mean was 7.8 miles, and the standard deviation of the sampling distribution was 1.6 miles.

Talk the Talk

1. What is the difference between a sample and a sampling distribution?

2. What is the difference between a sample proportion and a sample mean?

Online Time Study, Part III

To summarize data from a sample survey, observational study, or experiment:

- Calculate measures of center.

- Calculate measures of spread.

- Select the most appropriate method(s) to display the data (dot plot, histogram, stem-and-leaf plot, box-and-whisker plot, normal curve).

- Describe the characteristics of the graphical display.

How can you apply your new knowledge from this lesson to analyze data in the Online Time Study?

To analyze data from a sample survey, observational study, or experiment:

- Use confidence intervals to determine a range of values for the population mean(s) or proportion(s).

Recall the study described in previous lessons about the amount of time students in your school are online each day.

1. Will your study involve estimating a population mean or a population proportion? Explain your reasoning.

2. Use a 95% confidence interval to determine a range of values for the population mean, given a random sample of 60 students with a sample mean of 3.5 hours and a standard deviation of 1.1.

3. Use the sample mean and standard deviation of the sampling distribution to label the horizontal axis of the normal curve.

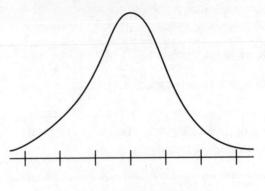

Average Time Spent Online

 Be prepared to share your results and methods.

How Much Different?

Using Statistical Significance to Make Inferences About Populations

A person's blood pressure is typically measured using two numbers. One number represents the pressure in the arteries when the heart beats. This is the systolic pressure. The other number represents the pressure in the arteries between heartbeats. This is the diastolic pressure. For example, $\frac{118}{74}$ represents a systolic pressure of 118 and a diastolic pressure of 74.

Whatta Water: Exploring Categorical Data

Commercials on a local TV station claim that Whatta Water tastes better than tap water, but a local news anchor does not believe the claim. She sets up an experiment at a local grocery store to test the claim. A representative, unbiased sample of 120 shoppers participate in the tasting survey using unmarked cups. Out of the 120 people, 64 said Whatta Water tastes better than tap water.

1. If shoppers had to choose one or the other and there was no difference in the tastes of the two waters, what proportion of shoppers would you expect to say that Whatta Water tastes better? Explain your reasoning.

2. What is the sample proportion of shoppers who stated that Whatta Water tastes better?

3. Based on your answers to Questions 1 and 2, what reason(s) can you give to doubt Whatta Water's claim? Explain your reasoning.

The term **statistically significant** is used to indicate that a result is very unlikely to have occurred by chance. Typically, a result that is more than 2 standard deviations from the mean, or outside a 95% confidence interval, is considered statistically significant.

Two standard deviations from the mean seems to come up a lot!

4. Use a 95% confidence interval to determine a range of values for the population proportion of people who prefer the taste of Whatta Water. Explain your work.

5. Use the sample proportion and standard deviation of the sampling distribution to label the horizontal axis of the normal curve.

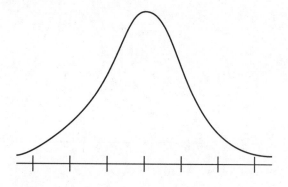

Percent Who Prefer Whatta Water to Tap Water

6. Based on the range of values of the 95% confidence interval, what conclusion can you make about Whatta Water's claim that their water tastes better than tap water?

7. The local water company also conducted a survey of 120 people which they said showed that people prefer tap water over Whatta Water. Forty-one of the respondents said Whatta Water tastes better.

The assumption again is that the results will be 50% if there is no difference between the two kinds of water.

a. Use a 95% confidence interval to determine a range of values for the population proportion of people who prefer Whatta Water. Explain your work.

b. Use the sample proportion and standard deviation of the sampling distribution to label the horizontal axis of the normal curve.

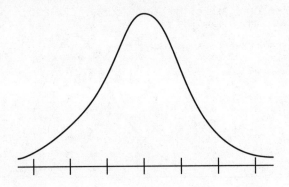

Percent Preferring Whatta Water

c. Based on the range of values of the 95% confidence interval, what conclusion can you draw about the local water company's claim that tap water tastes better than Whatta Water?

8. Use a random number generator to conduct a simulation of the local water company's survey, for a new sample of 120 people. Generate a random number between 1 and 100, with numbers from 1 to 34 representing that Whatta Water tastes better and numbers from 35 to 100 representing that tap water tastes better. List the results in the table.

Percent of People in Simulation Who Said Whatta Water Tastes Better	Percent of People in Simulation Who Said Tap Water Tastes Better

9. On the normal curve in Question 7 part (b), locate and mark the sample proportion of your simulation. Describe the location of the sample proportion on the normal curve.

10. Compare the results of your simulation with the water company's study and with Whatta Water's study. Are your results significantly different? Explain your reasoning.

Nonstop Homework: Exploring Continuous Data

A sample of 40 students at High Marks High School responded to a survey about the average amount of time spent on homework each day. The sample mean was 2.9 hours and the sample standard deviation was 0.8 hour.

This problem is similar to the last problem, only using continuous data instead of discrete data.

1. Use a 95% confidence interval to determine a range of values for the population mean. Explain your work.

2. Label the horizontal axis of the normal curve that represents the sampling distribution.

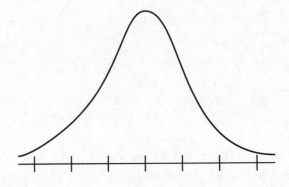

Mean Hours Spent on Homework

3. A new sample of 40 students was taken and the resulting sample mean was 2.70 hours.

   a. On the normal curve in Question 2, locate and mark the sample mean of the new sample. Describe the location of the sample mean on the normal curve.

b. Are the results of the new sample statistically significant? Explain your reasoning.

4. What sample mean values are statistically significant? Explain your reasoning.

5. Mary shared a comment about the time she spends on homework.

> Mary
>
> I spend an average of 3.5 hours on homework every night. Compared to the sample mean, the average amount of time I spend on homework every night is statistically significant.

Is Mary's reasoning valid? Explain why or why not.

Read Between the Lines: Comparing Categorical Data

Two hometown newspapers conducted a poll about whether residents are for or against a tax to provide funding for school renovations in the district. Today's News polled 75 residents and 53 stated that they are in favor of the tax increase. Local Time polled 100 residents and 54 stated they are in favor of the tax increase.

1. Calculate the sample proportion for each poll.

2. Use the results from each poll to estimate a range of values for the population proportion using a 95% confidence interval. Explain your work.

3. The Reporter newspaper published a survey of 90 residents and 38 stated that they are in favor of the tax increase. Use a 95% confidence interval to determine a range of values for the population proportion. Explain your work.

If two confidence intervals overlap, then the difference between the population proportions or population means is not statistically significant. If the intervals do not overlap then the difference between the population proportions or population means is statistically significant.

4. Compare the population proportion estimates and determine whether their differences are statistically significant. Explain your reasoning.

   a. The Reporter and Local Times

   b. The Reporter and Today's News

A researcher conducted a randomized experiment to see whether there was a link between a new supplement and blood pressure. She collected data from a representative, unbiased sample of 200 people who had high blood pressure. One hundred of the people were randomly selected to take the supplement and the other 100 people were given a placebo. Recall that a placebo is a treatment that is assumed to have no real effect on the characteristic of interest.

This experiment has two treatments: taking the supplement and taking the placebo.

The participants' blood pressures were recorded at the beginning and at the end of the 12-week experiment, and the difference (end − beginning) was calculated.

1. For the 100-person treatment that took the placebo, what value would you expect for the difference of sample means at the beginning of the experiment and at the end of the experiment. Explain your reasoning.

2. For the 100-person treatment that took the supplement, what value would you expect for the difference of sample means at the beginning of the experiment and at the end of the experiment. Explain your reasoning.

Suppose that the mean difference in blood pressure of the group who took the supplement was -15 with a standard deviation of 3.2, and the mean difference in blood pressure of the group who took the placebo was 1.7 with a standard deviation of 0.3.

3. Interpret and explain the meaning of a negative mean difference for the treatment that took the supplement and a positive mean difference for the treatment that took the placebo.

4. Use a 95% confidence interval to determine a range of values for the population mean of each treatment. Explain your work.

5. What conclusion can you make about whether or not the supplement effectively lowers high blood pressure? Explain your reasoning.

The results of an experiment may indicate a correlation but not a causation. Do you remember the difference?

PROBLEM 5 ## Decisions, Decisions . . .

1. A manufacturing company has a policy that states that if significantly more than 2% of computer parts are defective during an 8-hour shift, then the parts from that shift will not be shipped. During an 8 hour shift, 1020 parts were produced and 22 were defective. Should the parts be shipped? Explain your reasoning.

2. The mean grade point average (GPA) of a random sample of 50 High Mark High School students who had a part-time job during the previous grading period is 3.15 with a standard deviation of 0.44. The mean GPA of a random sample of 50 High Mark High School students who did not have a part-time job during the previous grading period is 2.77 with a standard deviation of 0.35. Does that data suggest a possible link between High Mark High School students' part-time job status and their GPA?

Recall the problem from the previous lesson about part-time job status and grade point average (GPA).

The population mean interval for the GPA of High Mark High School students who have a part-time job, 3.03 to 3.27, does not overlap with population mean interval for the GPA of High Mark High School students who do not have a part-time job, 2.67 to 2.87.

1. Carmen shared a conclusion about part-time job status and GPA.

> Carmen
>
> Because the results of the statistical analysis are statistically significant, I can conclude that holding a part-time job will result in a higher GPA.

Is Carmen's statement correct? Explain why or why not.

The interval for the estimate of the population mean for the GPA of neighboring Great Beginnings High School students who do not have a part-time job is 3.18 to 3.39.

2. Is the GPA of students who do not have a part-time job statistically different at High Mark High and Great Beginnings High School? Explain your reasoning.

3. The estimate for the population mean for the math GPA of Great Beginnings High School students using a sample of the math club is 3.27 to 3.54. The estimate for the population mean for the math GPA of Great Beginnings High School students using a sample of the government club is 3.11 to 3.40.

> **Max**
>
> The results of the statistical analysis are not statistically significant because the population mean intervals for math GPA overlap.

Is Max's statement correct? Explain why or why not.

Online Time Study, Part IV

To analyze data from a sample survey, observational study, or experiment, you can use statistical significance to make inferences about populations.

Recall the study you have been planning about the amount of time students in your school are online each day.

How can you use statistical significance to make inferences in the Online Time Study?

Suppose two samples of data were collected. One sample of 40 students in your school has a sample mean of 2.3 hours and a standard deviation of 0.7 hour. Another sample of 40 students in your school has a sample mean of 3.7 hours and a standard deviation of 1.1 hours.

1. Use a 95% confidence interval to determine whether the estimate of the population means using each sample is statistically significant. Explain your work.

Be prepared to share your results and methods.

DIY

Designing a Study and Analyzing the Results

In this lesson, you will:

- Analyze the validity of conclusions based on statistical analysis of data.
- Design a sample survey, observational study, or experiment to answer a question.
- Conduct a sample survey, observational study, or experiment to collect data.
- Summarize the data of your sample survey, observational study, or experiment.
- Analyze the data of your sample survey, observational study, or experiment.
- Summarize the results and justify conclusions of your sample survey, observational study, or experiment.

DIY stands for "do it yourself." So, why not? Try to write an interesting opener yourself for this lesson. Use these hints to help you get started:

- Make your opener related to something about the lesson or the whole chapter.
- Write about something you think other students would be interested in reading.
- Be creative!

Share your opener with your classmates. Which one did you like best?

Use the following guidelines to design and conduct a sample survey, observational study, or experiment, summarize and analyze the data, and draw conclusions. You can use this page as a checklist while planning and conducting your study.

I. Design a sample survey, observational study, or experiment.	
• Select a characteristic of interest to learn about from a sample survey, observational study, or experiment.	
• Select a question that can be answered by collecting quantitative data.	
• Identify the population.	
• Identify the characteristic being studied.	
• Describe the method for choosing a random sample.	
• Address potential sources of bias.	
II. Conduct the sample survey, observational study, or experiment.	
• Use the sampling method to collect data for your sample survey, observational study, or experiment.	
III. Summarize the data of the sample survey, observational study, or experiment.	
• Calculate measures of center.	
• Calculate measures of spread.	
• Select the most appropriate method(s) to display the data (dot plot, histogram, stem-and-leaf plot, box-and-whisker plot, normal curve).	
• Describe the characteristics of the graphical display.	
IV. Analyze the data of the sample survey, observational study, or experiment.	
• Use confidence intervals to determine a range of values for the population mean(s) or proportion(s).	
• Using statistical significance to make inferences about populations.	
V. Draw conclusions based on the results of the sample survey, observational study, or experiment.	
• Write a conclusion that answers the question of interest of your sample survey, observational study, or experiment. Use the data and data analysis to justify your conclusion.	

Be prepared to share your results and methods.

KEY TERMS

- characteristic of interest (2.1)
- sample survey (2.1)
- random sample (2.1)
- biased sample (2.1)
- observational study (2.1)
- experiment (2.1)
- treatment (2.1)
- experimental unit (2.1)
- confounding (2.1)

- convenience sample (2.2)
- subjective sample (2.2)
- volunteer sample (2.2)
- simple random sample (2.2)
- stratified random sample (2.2)
- cluster sample (2.2)
- cluster (2.2)

- systematic sample (2.2)
- parameter (2.2)
- statistic (2.2)
- population proportion (2.3)
- sample proportion (2.3)
- sampling distribution (2.3)
- confidence interval (2.3)
- statistically significant (2.4)

2.1 Identifying Characteristics of Sample Surveys, Observational Studies, and Experiments

The characteristic of interest is the specific question to be answered or the specific information to be gathered for sample surveys, observational studies, and experiments. The entire set of items from which data can be selected is the population. A subset of the population that is selected is a sample.

Example

Fifty-five deer are randomly selected from a park in the township. They are anesthetized, weighed, and then released back into the park.

The population is all of the deer in the park. The sample is the 55 deer selected. The characteristic of interest is the mean weight of the deer.

Differentiating Between Sample Surveys, Observational Studies, and Experiments

A sample survey poses a question of interest to a sample of the targeted population. An observational study gathers data about a characteristic of the population without trying to influence the data. An experiment gathers data on the effect of one or more treatments on the characteristic of interest.

Example

A study states that approximately 78% of planes arrived on time during a 3 hour period at an airport.

This is an observational study since the study only gathered data about the number of planes that arrived on time and did not try to influence the data.

2.2 Using a Variety of Sampling Methods to Collect Data

Sampling methods could include convenience sampling, volunteer sampling, simple random sampling, stratified random sampling, cluster sampling, and systematic sampling.

Example

The data set below shows the number of late student arrivals at four elementary schools each week for five weeks.

Number of Late Arrivals				
Week 1	Week 2	Week 3	Week 4	Week 5
49	37	45	44	43
47	41	45	46	48
39	43	38	44	42
43	47	39	39	42
52	55	50	54	55

You can create a stratified random sample with 5 data values to describe the number of late arrivals by randomly choosing one school from each of the 5 weeks and recording the number of late arrivals: {39, 37, 50, 46, 42}.

Identifying Factors of Sampling Methods that could Contribute to Gathering Biased Data

Some sampling methods introduces bias, which reduces the likelihood of a representative, unbiased sample.

Example

A cereal company conducts taste tests for a new cereal on a random sample of its employees.

There is bias in this study because the taste test is only conducted on the company's employees. It is possible that the employees will prefer the cereal of the company that employs them for other reasons than taste.

 Exploring, Identifying, and Interpreting the Role of Randomization in Sampling

You can use random sampling by using a random digit table or a graphing calculator to create unbiased samples.

Example

For the data set, you can use a calculator to generate four random numbers between 1 and 10. Then you can use the numbers generated to create a random sample of four from the data set.

The 25-meter freestyle times, in seconds, of ten young swimmers are shown.

Swimmer	1	2	3	4	5	6	7	8	9	10
Time	21.2	19.3	18.7	20.6	20.5	18.4	22.9	23.5	18.2	17.9

Possible random numbers: 19.3, 18.7, 22.9, 17.9.

2.3 Recognizing that Data from Samples are Used to Estimate Population Proportions and Population Means

Data from samples are used to calculate confidence intervals that estimate population proportions and population means.

Example

A sample of 250 women responded to a survey about the amount of money they spend on cosmetics each month. The sample mean was $45.50 and the sample standard deviation was $10.75.

The interval from $44.14 to $46.86 represents a 95% confidence interval for the population mean.

$$\frac{s}{\sqrt{n}} = \frac{10.75}{\sqrt{250}} \approx 0.68$$

2.4 Using Sample Proportions to Determine Whether Differences in Population Proportions are Statistically Significant

To determine the sample proportions that would be statistically significant, use the normal curve and label it based on the standard deviation from the sample.

Example

Use the sample proportion and standard deviation of the sampling distribution to label the horizontal axis of the normal curve. Then, determine what sample proportions would be statistically significant.

A sample proportion of families that own dogs is 74%, and the standard deviation is 0.017.

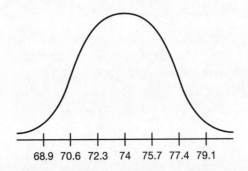

68.9 70.6 72.3 74 75.7 77.4 79.1

Sample proportion values less than 70.6% and greater than 77.4% are statistically significant because those values are outside of the 95% confidence interval.

2.4 Using Sample Means to Determine Whether Differences in Population Means are Statistically Significant

Use the sample mean and standard deviation to determine the margin of error for the confidence interval. The margin of error is 2 times the standard deviation.

Example

Use a 95% confidence interval to determine a range of values for the population mean. Explain your work.

A sample of 80 doctors took a stress test. The sample mean was 44.5 and the sample standard deviation was 14.8.

The interval from 41.2 to 44.5 represents a 95% confidence interval for the population mean.

The margin of error is approximately ±3.30.

$$\frac{s}{\sqrt{n}} = \frac{14.8}{\sqrt{80}} \approx 1.65$$

$$2(1.65) = 3.30$$

2.5 Conducting a Sample Survey, Observational Study, or Experiment to Answer a Question

You can determine what type of sample technique would be most appropriate to answer a question for a sample survey, observational study, or experiment.

Example

Suppose you want to estimate the number of senior citizens in a town that are on public assistance.

You can assign all the senior citizens in the town an ID number and use a computer to randomly generate a sample of senior citizens. This technique provides a random sample of the population of the senior citizens in the town, and random sampling is typically representative of a population.

Searching for Patterns

3

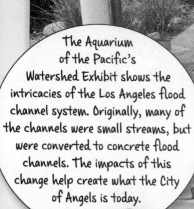

The Aquarium of the Pacific's Watershed Exhibit shows the intricacies of the Los Angeles flood channel system. Originally, many of the channels were small streams, but were converted to concrete flood channels. The impacts of this change help create what the City of Angels is today.

Patterns: They're Grrrrrowing!

Exploring and Analyzing Patterns

In this lesson, you will:

- Identify multiple patterns within a sequence.
- Use patterns to solve problems.

Y ou can find patterns everywhere! Sometimes you can describe them in terms of color, shape, size or texture. Other times, a pattern's beauty isn't evident until you describe it using mathematics.

Let's consider a pattern found in nature—the family tree of a male drone bee. Female bees have two parents, a male and a female whereas male bees have just one parent, a female. In this family tree the parents appear below the original male drone bee.

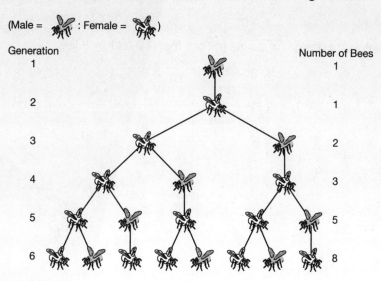

The total number of bees in each generation follows the pattern:

1, 1, 2, 3, 5, 8, . . .

What makes this particular pattern fascinating is that it seems to appear everywhere! This pattern is called the Fibonacci Sequence and you can find it in flowers, seashells, pineapples, art, architecture, and even in your DNA!

Do you see the pattern? If so, name the next three terms.

Terrance owns a flooring company. His latest job involves tiling a square room. Terrance's customer, Mr. Rivera, requests a tile pattern of alternating black, white, and gray tiles as shown. Each tile is one square foot.

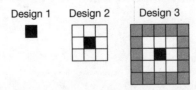

Design 1   Design 2   Design 3

1. Analyze Terrance's design of a tile pattern for a square floor. Describe as many patterns as you can.

2. Sketch the design for a square floor that is 9 feet by 9 feet.

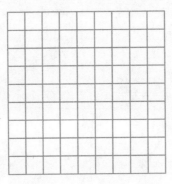

Remember, each tile is one square foot.

3. Describe the key features of Design 8 of a square floor. Write as many key features as you can.

A table might help you organize the various patterns you noticed in Question 1.

Design	1	2	3	4	5	6	7	8
Square Dimensions								
Edge Color								
Number of Black Tiles								
Number of White Tiles								
Number of Gray Tiles								
Total Tiles								

4. A hotel manager wants Terrance to tile their lobby using the same design he created for Mr. Rivera. The lobby measures 45 feet by 45 feet. He wants the outer edge to be the same color as the center tile. Will this occur? Justify your answer.

Think about how you can work backwards to get to this answer efficiently.

5. Very picky Paula Perkins requests a tile floor from Terrance. She also wants the alternating black, white, and gray tile pattern; however, she wants the outer edge of the tile to match her wall color. The room is 101 feet by 101 feet and the wall color is white. What color must the center tile be to ensure the outer edge is white? Show or explain your work.

How can you predict what will happen without doing all of the calculations?

The class president, vice president, and treasurer of a high school count the ballots for the homecoming king election. The election result is generally kept a secret until the pep rally, when the winner is announced in front of the entire senior class. Unfortunately, this year's ballot counters are not very good at keeping a secret. The very next day, each ballot counter tells two of their friends in the senior class the election result, but makes each friend vow not to spread the result. However, each of the ballot counter's friends cannot keep a secret either. The following day each friend of each ballot counter shares the election result with two of their friends in the senior class. This pattern continues for the entire week leading up to the pep rally.

> Let's assume that no student is told the result of the election twice.

1. Create a visual model to represent this problem situation. Describe the patterns you observe.

2. How many new seniors will know the winner of the homecoming king election on the fourth day? Explain your reasoning.

3. The total number of students in the senior class is 250. If the ballot counters knew the election result on Monday, will every senior already know the winner of the election when the result is announced at the pep rally 6 days later? Explain your reasoning.

Maureen and Matthew are designing their backyard patio. There will be an entrance and exit off the front and back of the patio. The sequence shown represents different designs depending on the size of the patio.

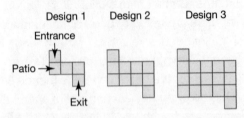

 1. Analyze each design in the sequence. Describe as many patterns as you can.

2. Sketch Design 6 of the sequence.

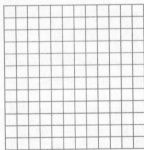

3. Matthew has 180 tiles he can use for this project. Identify the largest patio design that he can make. Show or explain your reasoning.

 Be prepared to share your solutions and methods.

Are They Saying the Same Thing?

Using Patterns to Generate Algebraic Expressions

LEARNING GOALS

In this lesson, you will:

- Generate algebraic expressions using geometric patterns.
- Represent algebraic expressions in different forms.
- Determine whether expressions are equivalent.
- Identify patterns as linear, exponential, or quadratic using a visual model, a table of values, or a graph.

Are natural habits hard to break? The answer for most grocery stores would be, "Why in the world would we break these habits?" This is the reason why many grocery stores have followed a tried-and-true way for laying out their items in the aisles. Studies have shown that most Americans tend to prefer to shop in a counter-clockwise pattern; thus, most grocery stores have their produce at the front and to the right of the entrance which then leads (in a counter-clockwise manner) toward the bakery. And more cleverly, the bakery is toward the middle or the back of the store. From here, many stores lead you to the meat section and then the dairy section. So, why are the bakery, meat, and dairy sections toward the back of the store? Once again, grocery stores embrace people's natural tendencies. For most families, the most needed items are meats, breads, and milk. So, when these items are toward the back of the store, it provides more chances for customers to make "impulse" purchases along the way—buying things that weren't on the original grocery list!

While scientists don't know what causes this impulse (moving in a counter-clockwise manner, or buying items that aren't necessarily needed), it is extremely strong.

This impulse to move in a counter-clockwise direction can be thought of as a pattern similar to animal migrations. Is this the only way to get to where you are going? Of course not, but for some reason, it seems to be a more comfortable path. When problem solving in mathematics there are often many ways for you to approach a problem, but usually you choose a familiar method. Do you usually find one way to do something and then stick with it, or do you look for different methods?

PROBLEM 1 **Floors by Terrance**

Terrance's flooring business from the problem, *There's More Than One Way to Tile a Floor*, was booming! He decides to hire several employees to help lay out his tile designs. It will be necessary for Terrance to describe his tile designs in a clear manner so that all of the employees can create them correctly. Recall that Terrance's square floor design uses alternating black, white, and gray tiles.

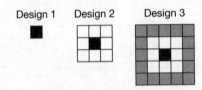

Design 1   Design 2   Design 3

 1. Describe the pattern in terms of the number of new tiles that must be added to each new square floor design.

2. Write an expression to represent the number of new tiles that must be added to an *n* by *n* square floor design. Let *n* represent the number of tiles along each edge of the square.

 3. Describe which values for *n* make sense in this problem situation?

4. Ramone determined an expression to represent this pattern. His expression and explanation are shown.

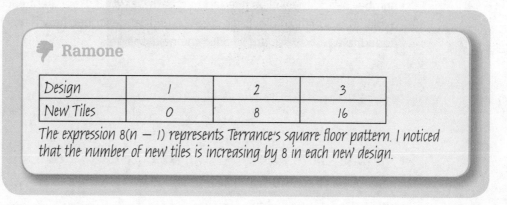

> **Ramone**
>
> | Design | 1 | 2 | 3 |
> | --- | --- | --- | --- |
> | New Tiles | 0 | 8 | 16 |
>
> The expression $8(n - 1)$ represents Terrance's square floor pattern. I noticed that the number of new tiles is increasing by 8 in each new design.

Explain why Ramone's expression is incorrect.

5. Describe the pattern as new tiles are added as linear, quadratic, exponential, or none of these. Explain your reasoning.

6. Terrance asks his employees to determine the number of new tiles added to Design 2 to create Design 3. Each employee describes a unique method to determine the number of additional tiles needed to create Design 3. Represent each of his employee's explanations with an algebraic expression that describes how many new tiles must be added to an $n \times n$ square to build the next design.

Wilma

I must add 3 tiles to each of the four sides of the white square, which is 4 · 3 tiles. Then I must add 1 tile at each corner. So the number of additional tiles added to a Design 2 square floor design is 4 · 3 + 4.

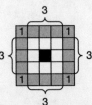

Expression: _____

Howard

I must add 5 tiles to two of the sides and 3 tiles to the other two sides. The number of additional tiles added to Design 2 square floor design is 2(3 + 2) + 2 · 3.

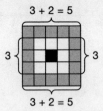

Expression: _____

Tyler

I need to add 3 tiles four times and then add the four corner tiles. The number of additional tiles added to Design 2 square floor design is 3 + 3 + 3 + 3 + 4.

Expression: _____

Tamara

The way I look at it, I really have two squares. The original square for Design 2 has 3 · 3 tiles. The newly formed Design 3 square has 5 · 5 tiles. So, the number of additional tiles added to the Design 2 square floor design is 5 · 5 − 3 · 3.

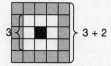

Expression: _____

7. Which expression do you think Terrance should use? Explain your reasoning.

> Does the expression you determined match one of the expressions Terrance's employees determined?

8. Michael and Louise analyze the expressions they wrote for each student. They both determined that the expression to represent Tamara's method is $(n + 2)^2 - n^2$. Michael claims that this expression is quadratic because of the n^2 term. Louise disagrees and says the expression is linear because the pattern is linear.
Who is correct? Explain your reasoning.

9. Use each expression you determined in Question 6 to calculate the number of tiles that must be added to squares with side lengths of 135 tiles to create the next design.

Wilma's expression: Tyler's expression:

Howard's expression: Tamara's expression:

10. Wilma tells Terrance that since all of the expressions resulted in the same solution, any of the expressions can be used to determine the number of additional tiles needed to make more $n \times n$ designs. Terrance thinks that the employees need to use more values in the expressions than just one to make this conclusion.
Who is correct? Explain your reasoning.

Recall that two or more algebraic expressions are equivalent if they produce the same output for all input values. You can verify that two expressions are equivalent by using properties to rewrite the two expressions as the same expression.

11. Show that Wilma, Howard, Tyler, and Tamara's expressions are equivalent. Justify your reasoning.

Let's revisit the problem, *Can You Keep a Secret?* about the homecoming king election. The visual model shown represents the number of new seniors who learn about the election result each day that passes.

1. Analyze the pattern.

   a. Complete the table to summarize the number of new seniors who learn about the election result each day. Then write an expression to represent the number of new seniors who learn about the election result on the *n*th day. Finally, describe how each part of your expression relates to the visual model.

Number of Days That Pass	Number of Seniors Who Hear the Results That Day
1	
2	
3	
4	
5	
6	
n	

b. Create a graph of the data from your table on the coordinate plane shown. Then draw a smooth curve to model the relationship between the number of days that pass and the number of seniors who hear the senior election results.

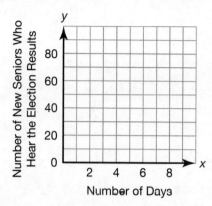

2. Do all the points on the smooth curve make sense in terms of this problem situation? Why or why not?

When you model a relationship on a coordinate plane with a smooth curve, it is up to you to consider the situation and interpret the meaning of the data values shown.

3. Describe this pattern as linear, exponential, quadratic, or none of these. Then write the corresponding equation. How does each representation support your answer?

4. Describe the key characteristics of your graph. Explain each characteristic algebraically and in terms of this problem situation.

5. After how many days will 500 new seniors learn about the election results?

6. Determine the number of seniors who hear the election results on the twelfth day. Does your answer make sense in the context of this problem? Explain your reasoning.

Several Spreading Sequences of Squares

 Let's revisit the problem, *How Large Is Your Yard?* about backyard patio designs. The model shown represents the first three designs Maureen and Matthew could use. Each square represents 1 square foot.

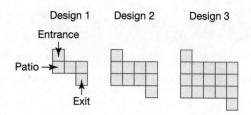

 1. Determine the number of squares in the next two patio designs of the pattern.

 2. Write an expression to determine the total number of squares in patio Design *n*. Describe how each part of your expression relates to the visual model.

3. Maureen and Matthew each write different expressions to represent the patio designs.

a.

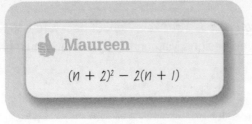

Maureen

$$(n + 2)^2 - 2(n + 1)$$

Describe how each term in Maureen's expression represents the visual model.

Maureen's expression uses subtraction. How can she take away tiles if the number of tiles in each term is increasing?

b.

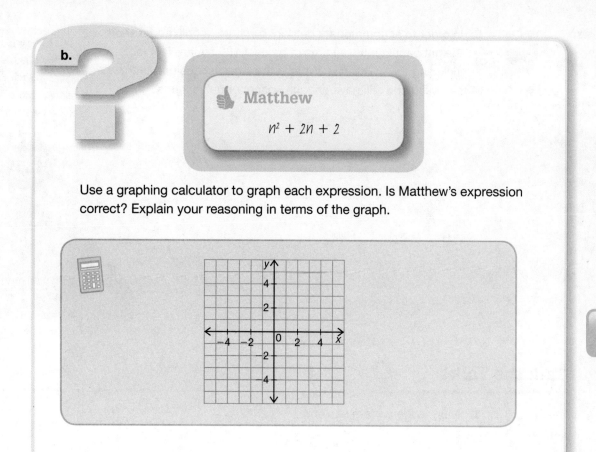

Matthew

$$n^2 + 2n + 2$$

Use a graphing calculator to graph each expression. Is Matthew's expression correct? Explain your reasoning in terms of the graph.

4. Identify the parts of the graph that represent this problem situation.

5. In order to accommodate outdoor furniture, a grill, and a shed, the patio must have an area of at least 125 square feet (not including the walkways). What is the smallest design Matthew can build and still have enough space for these items?

How is the number of tiles in each design related to the one that came before it?

Talk the Talk

1. Analyze the pattern shown.

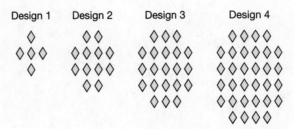

a. Identify two expressions that represent the total number of diamonds used to construct Design *n*.

b. Describe how your expressions relate to the visual model.

c. Algebraically prove your expressions are equivalent.

d. Graphically show that your expressions are equivalent.

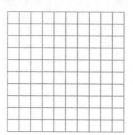

2. Describe the ways you can prove any two expressions are equivalent.

 Be prepared to share your solutions and methods.

Are All Functions Created Equal?

Comparing Multiple Representations of Functions

LEARNING GOALS

In this lesson, you will:

- Identify equivalent forms of functions in various representations.
- Model situations using tables, graphs, and equations.
- Use functions to make predictions.
- Determine whether two forms of a function are equivalent.

KEY TERMS

- relation
- function
- function notation

Every year during the first full week in August, the residents of Twinsburg, Ohio literally see double! That's because Twinsburg hosts the annual Twin Day Festival. It is the largest gathering of twins in the world, with thousands of twins, triplets, and multiple-birth families converging on the town for a weekend of games and activities. Although twins develop their own unique personalities, they often stand out in a crowd. It might be an interesting experience for twins and non-twins alike to be in a town completely filled with groups of people who look the same. *Not* having a person who looks just like you might actually make you stand out in the crowd.

Twins only account for about 1% of the pregnancies in the world, but the number of twin births actually varies depending on where you live. For example, the rate of twin births in Massachusetts is much higher than the rate in New Mexico. The highest rates in the world are found in central Africa while the lowest rates are found in Asia.

What do you think might account for differences throughout the world in the rate of twin births? Have you ever known twins? Would you like to have a twin brother or sister?

Understanding patterns not only gives insight into the world around you, it provides you with a powerful tool for predicting the future. Pictures, words, graphs, tables, and equations can describe the exact same pattern, but in different ways.

A relation is a mapping between a set of input values and a set of output values. In the problem, *The Cat's Out of the Bag*, you used a visual model, graph, table, and context to describe the relation between the number of ballot counters, and the total number of seniors that learned the result of the homecoming king election. In relations such as this one, there is only one output for each input. This type of relation is called a *function*. A **function** is a relation such that for each element of the domain there exists exactly one element in the range. **Function notation** is a way to represent functions algebraically. The function $f(x)$ is read as "f of x" and indicates that x is the input and $f(x)$ is the output.

> Remember that the domain is the set of all the input values and the range is the set of all the output values.

Directions: Cut out the relations provided on the following pages. You will encounter graphs, tables, equations, and contexts. Analyze and then sort the relations into groups of equivalent representations. All relations will have at least one match.

Attach your groupings on the blank pages that follow the cut-out pages. Then provide a brief rationale for how you grouped each set of relations.

> Be careful— all groupings do not necessarily have the same number of representations. Also, remember that equations can be written in different forms and still be equivalent.

A

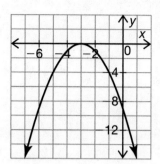

B

$f(x) = x^2 + 2x + 5$

C

x	y
1	2
2	4
3	6
4	8
5	10

D

$f(x) = x^2 + 6x + 5$

E

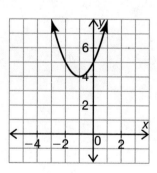

F

$f(x) = -(x^2 + 6x + 9)$

G

$f(x) = 2x$

H

$f(x) = (x + 5)(x + 1)$

I

$f(x) = -(x + 3)(x + 3)$

J

A relation with a line of symmetry at $x = -3$, a vertex that is a maximum value, and a graph that opens down.

K

Louise heard a rumor. She tells the rumor to two people the next day. The two people that she told then tell two more people the following day, who each then go on to tell two more new people the rumor the following day. The relationship between the days that have passed and the number of new people who hear the rumor that day.

L

x	y
−3	8
−2	5
−1	4
0	5
1	8

M

x	y
−4	−1
−3	0
−2	−1
−1	−4
0	−9

N

$$y = 2^x$$

O

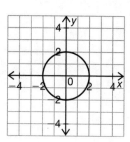

P

$$y = (x + 3)^2 - 4$$

Q

x	y
0	1
1	2
2	4
3	8
4	16

R

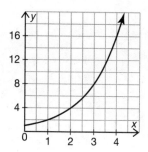

S

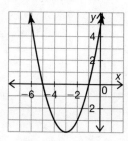

T

U

Erika is worried that her secret got out. On the first day she and her best friend were the only people who knew about the secret. But now, two new people are finding out the secret every day. The relationship between the number of days that have passed and the total number of people who know about her secret.

V

$$x^2 + y^2 = 4$$

W

x	y
−5	0
−4	−3
0	5
1	12
2	21

X

x	y
−1	1.73
−1	−1.73
0	2
0	−2
1	1.73
1	−1.73

3

1. What strategies did you use to sort the representations into your groups?

Did you come up with more than one way to show that different representations are equivalent?

2. How do you know which relations are functions and which are not functions? Explain your reasoning in terms of the graph, table, and equation.

3. Identify the function family associated with each grouping. How can you determine the function family from the graph, table, context, and the equation?

A ceramic tile company creates a new line of decorative kitchen and bathroom tiles. The company will sell larger tiles that are created from combinations of small gray and white square tiles. The designs follow the pattern shown.

Design 1   Design 2   Design 3

        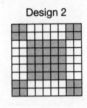   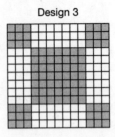

1. Analyze the tile designs. Describe all of the various patterns that you notice.

 2. Numerically organize the pattern.

Design Number	1	2	3	4	7	10	
Number of White Tiles, $w(n)$							
Number of Gray Tiles, $g(n)$							
Total Number of Tiles, $t(n)$							

3. What new patterns do you notice?

Don't worry about the last column for now. You will determine an expression for each type of tile later.

4. How many total tiles are in Design 7? How many of the tiles are white? How many are gray? Explain your reasoning.

5. A hotel would like to order the largest design possible. They have enough money in their budget to order a design made up of 1700 total gray and white tiles. Which design can they afford? How many tiles in the design will be white? How many will be gray? Explain your reasoning.

6. Complete the last column of the table in Question 2 by writing an expression to describe the number of white tiles, gray tiles, and total tiles for Design n.

7. Tonya and Alex came up with different expressions to represent the number of gray tiles in each pattern. Their expressions are shown.

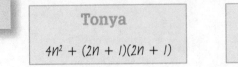

Tonya	Alex
$4n^2 + (2n + 1)(2n + 1)$	$(4n + 1)^2 - 4n(2n + 1)$

Tonya claims that they are the same expression written different ways. Alex says, "One expression has addition and the other has subtraction. There is no way they are equivalent!"

Who is correct? Justify your reasoning using algebraic and graphical representations.

You may have noticed several patterns in this sequence. An obvious pattern is that the sum of the white tiles and gray tiles is equal to the total number of tiles. This pattern is clear when analyzing the values in the table. However, adding $w(n)$ and $g(n)$ creates a brand new function that looks very different from the function $t(n)$.

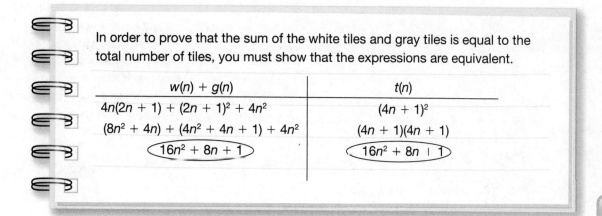

In order to prove that the sum of the white tiles and gray tiles is equal to the total number of tiles, you must show that the expressions are equivalent.

$w(n) + g(n)$	$t(n)$
$4n(2n + 1) + (2n + 1)^2 + 4n^2$	$(4n + 1)^2$
$(8n^2 + 4n) + (4n^2 + 4n + 1) + 4n^2$	$(4n + 1)(4n + 1)$
$\boxed{16n^2 + 8n + 1}$	$\boxed{16n^2 + 8n + 1}$

8. Analyze the context, table, and expressions in this problem.

   a. Identify the function family that describes the pattern for the number of white tiles. Explain your reasoning.

The best mathematicians work in teams to prove ideas. People often point to Andrew Wiles as an interesting exception, because he worked in his attic by himself for many years to prove Fermat's Last Theorem! In truth, though, even he occasionally collaborated with a friend. Look it up sometime—it's a fascinating story!

   b. Identify the function family that describes the pattern for the number of gray tiles. Explain your reasoning.

   c. When you add the functions that represent the number of gray tiles and white tiles, does the new function belong to the same function family? Explain your reasoning.

9. Describe the relationship between the number of white tiles and gray tiles in each design. Prove that this relationship exists.

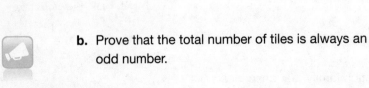

There are many ways to prove something. Mathematical proofs consist of equations, written arguments, pictures, and flow charts. Use correct terminology to describe mathematically why you know something is true.

10. Analyze the tile patterns.

    a. Prove that the number of white tiles is always an even number.

    b. Prove that the total number of tiles is always an odd number.

Talk the Talk

Choose a word that makes each statement true. Explain your reasoning.

always	sometimes	never

You can use a word more than once, or not at all. Choose wisely!

1. Two functions are _____ equivalent if their algebraic representations are the same.

2. Two functions are _____ equivalent if they produce the same output for a specific input value.

3. Two functions are _____ equivalent if their graphical representations are the same.

Be prepared to share your solutions and methods.

Water Under the Bridge
Modeling with Functions

LEARNING GOALS

In this lesson, you will:

- Use multiple representations of functions to model and solve problems.
- Use multiple representations of functions to analyze problems.

"It's just water under the bridge" is more than a saying for some hydrologists. To them, it's their career. Some hydrologists specialize in the design of city drainage systems.

So, you might be asking: how important is a city's drainage system? The key function to any drainage system is to channel rain water out of the area at the maximum speed possible. In the early part of the 20th century, the Los Angeles River routinely jumped its banks causing some areas of the city to flood. Outraged citizens demanded a better means of draining water after torrential rains. Hydrologists at the time decided to convert the Los Angeles River from a natural river to a massive storm drain. By pouring concrete and building up the sides of the drain, the city no longer flooded. However, the water that rushes through the drain can reach speeds of 45 miles per hour. These speeds are obviously very dangerous for anyone who might be in the storm drain system at the time of the storm. So while the drain has helped save the city from destruction caused by flooding, many lives have been lost as a result of citizens and rescuers being swept away in the drain system during a storm.

Do you think the city should raise the height of the drain so fewer people fall in? Would that affect how quickly the water flows through the drain?

A nearby town hired a civil engineer to rebuild their storm drainage system. The drains in this town are open at the top to allow water to flow directly into them. While designing the drains, the engineer must keep in mind the height and the width of the drain. She needs to consider the height because the water cannot rise above the drain or it will flood the town and cause major destruction. However the drain must also be wide enough that it will not get clogged by debris.

The civil engineer will use rectangular sheets of metal to build the drains. These sheets are bent up on both sides to represent the height of the drain. An end view of the drain is shown.

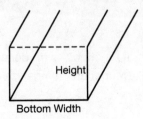

Height

Bottom Width

1. Use a sheet of paper to model a drain.

   a. Compare your model of a drain to your classmate's models. Identify similarities and differences between your models.

   b. How does folding the sides of the drain affect the bottom width of the drain?

   c. Describe the drain that you think best fits the needs of the town. Explain your reasoning.

The sheets of metal being used to create the drain are 8.5 feet wide. The engineer wants to identify possible heights and bottom width measurements she could use to construct the drains.

2. Determine the bottom width for each given height. Then complete the table by choosing different heights and calculating the bottom widths for those heights. If necessary, construct models of each drain.

Height of the Drain (feet)	Bottom Width of the Drain (feet)
0	
1.5	
3	

Which height values make sense for this situation?

3. Describe how to calculate the bottom width for any height.

4. Define a function $w(h)$ for the bottom width given a height of h feet.

 5. The engineer needs to identify the measurements that allow the most water to flow through the drain. What does the engineer need to calculate? What does she need to consider?

In order to determine the drain dimensions that allows the most water to flow through, the engineer must calculate the cross-sectional area. The cross-sectional area of a drain is shown.

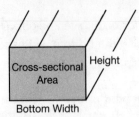

6. Describe how to determine the cross-sectional area of any drain.

Do I just use w for width? Didn't I already write a formula to determine width? Hmmmm maybe I should look back . . .

7. Predict and describe the drain with the maximum cross-sectional area.

8. Define a function $A(h)$ for the cross-sectional area of the drain with a height of h feet.

9. Use a graphing calculator to graph the function $A(h)$. Label your axes.

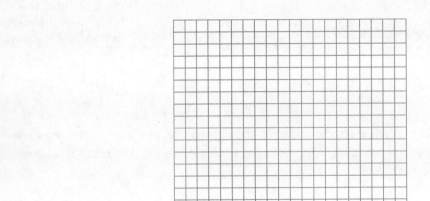

10. Analyze your graph.

a. What is the maximum cross-sectional area for the drain pipe? Explain your reasoning.

b. Identify the intercepts of $A(h)$. What does each mean in terms of this problem situation? Label each intercept on the graph.

c. Identify the equation of the axis of symmetry. Then label the axis of symmetry on the graph. Finally, describe the relationship between the axis of symmetry and the maximum cross-sectional area.

11. Draw and label the drain with the greatest cross-sectional area.

Is there a way to determine the maximum cross-sectional area using the x-intercepts?

12. In this problem you built a new function $A(h) = h(8.5 - 2h)$ using two existing functions.

   a. What is the first factor in this function? What does it represent in terms of this problem situation?

   b. What is the second factor in this function? What does it represent in terms of this problem situation?

   c. Identify the function families represented by each factor.

   d. When these factors are multiplied together what type of function is created? Why does this happen?

Determine the Best Design

 A civil engineering company is hired to design a new drainage system for your town. To construct one of the storm drains, a sheet of metal that is 15.25 feet wide is folded on both sides.

 Describe the drain that has the maximum cross-sectional area. Include at least two different representations in your description. Show all work and explain your reasoning.

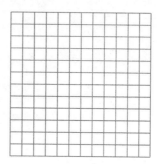

 Be prepared to share your solutions and methods.

I've Created a Monster, $m(x)$

Analyzing Graphs to Build New Functions

LEARNING GOALS

In this lesson, you will:

- Model operations on functions graphically.
- Sketch the graph of the sum, difference, and product of two functions on a coordinate plane.
- Predict and verify the graphical behavior of functions.
- Build functions graphically.
- Predict and verify the behavior of functions using a table of values.
- Build functions using a table of values.

KEY TERM

- Zero Product Property
- polynomial
- degree

In 1818 Mary Shelley wrote the science fiction novel *Frankenstein*. It is the tale of Dr. Victor Frankenstein, a scientist who dreams of creating life. He accomplishes this dream by using old body parts and electricity. Unfortunately, he creates a monster! Horrified and filled with regret, Victor decides that he must end the life that he created. His monster has other plans, though. He is lonely and wants Victor to create a woman to keep him company in this cruel world! Crime, drama, and vengeance follow as the creator struggles with his creation.

Frankenstein laid the foundation for many of the horror and science fiction movies that you see today. While Mary Shelley's novel is a literary classic for how it tackles deep issues such as the meaning of life and the ethics of creation, it is also good old-fashioned, scary fun. Do you enjoy scary movies? If so, do you think any of your favorites may have been influenced by this classic tale?

In the problem, *Why Are You So Square?* you added the functions $w(n)$ and $g(n)$ algebraically to create a new function $t(n)$. Manipulating algebraic representations is a common method for building new functions. However, you can also build new functions graphically. Let's consider two graphs of functions on a coordinate plane and what happens when you add, subtract, or multiply the output values of each.

1. Analyze the graphs of $f(x)$ and $g(x)$.

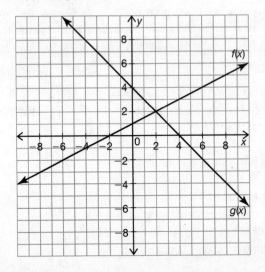

a. Predict the function family of $m(x)$ if $m(x) = f(x) + g(x)$. Explain your reasoning.

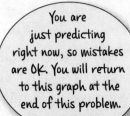

You are just predicting right now, so mistakes are OK. You will return to this graph at the end of this problem.

b. Predict and sketch the graph of $m(x)$.

c. Explain how you predicted the location of $m(x)$.

A graph of a function is a set of an infinite number of points. When you add two functions you are adding the output values for each input value. Given two functions, $f(x)$ and $g(x)$, on a coordinate plane, you can graphically add these functions to produce a new function, $m(x)$. To get started, let's consider what happens when you add $f(x)$ and $g(x)$ at a single point.

Let's add the output values for $f(x)$ and $g(x)$ at $x = 6$ to determine $(6, m(6))$.

$m(6) = f(6) + g(6)$
$m(6) = 4 + -2$
$m(6) = 2$

The point on the new function $m(x)$ is $(6, 2)$.

Other points on the graph of $m(x)$ can be determined in a similar way.

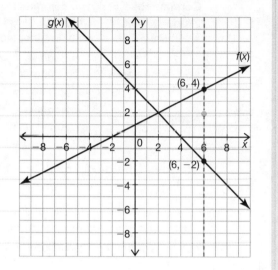

2. Analyze the addition of the output values for the input value $x = 6$ in the worked example.

   a. How is this process similar to adding integers on a number line?

   Drawing a vertical line can help you determine the two output values for a given input. Notice the x-values are the same in these points.

   b. Why is the point $(6, m(6))$ closer to $f(x)$ than $g(x)$?

   c. Why did the input value of 6 stay the same while the output values changed?

   d. Choose a different input value. Add the output values for $f(x)$ and $g(x)$ to determine a new point on the graph of $m(x)$.

Now, let's consider what happens when you add $f(x)$ and $g(x)$ at a few other points. The properties you use in integer operations also extend to operations on the graphs of functions. Recall the integer properties shown in the table.

Property	Definition	Integer Example
Commutative Property over Addition	The commutative property states that the order in which the terms are added does not change the sum. In other words $a + b = b + a$.	$35 + 43 = 43 + 35$
Additive Inverse	The additive inverse of a number is the number such that the sum of the given number and its additive inverse is 0.	The numbers -5 and 5 are additive inverses because $-5 + 5 = 0$.
Additive Identity	The additive identity is 0 because any number added to 0 is equal to itself.	$5 + 0 = 5$

3. Extend the integer properties from the table to operations on the graphs of functions.

   a. Use two output values from functions $f(x)$ and $g(x)$ to demonstrate the commutative property over addition for functions.

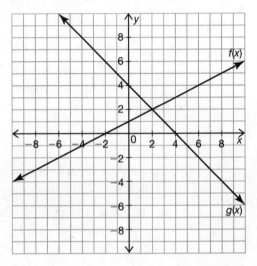

   b. Determine output values for $f(x)$ and $g(x)$ that demonstrate the Additive Inverse Property. Show that they are additive inverses algebraically and graphically.

   c. Determine output values for $f(x)$ and $g(x)$ that demonstrate the Additive Identity Property. Show that they are additive identities algebraically and graphically.

4. Ari and Will disagree over the location of $(2, m(2))$ when the output values of the functions $f(x)$ and $g(x)$ are added.

Ari	Will
$g(2) + f(2) = (2, m(2))$	$(2, 2) + 0 = (2, 2)$
$(2, 2) + (2, 2) = (2, 4)$	The location of $(2, m(2))$ is $(2, 2)$.
The location of $(2, m(2))$ is $(2, 4)$.	The lines intersect at one point.
The two points are at the intersection. Adding the output values of the two points equals $(2, 2 + 2)$.	A point plus zero is itself.

Who is correct? Explain your reasoning.

When performing operations on two graphs, it isn't practical to consider all sets of ordered pairs. The process is much more efficient if you use key points. Some of the points considered in this problem, such as intercepts, zeros, and intersection points, are good examples of key points.

5. Sketch the graph of $m(x) = f(x) + g(x)$.

   a. Circle key points of the graphs of $f(x)$ and $g(x)$.

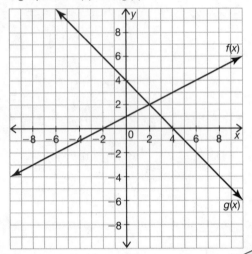

   b. Draw dashed vertical lines through your key points.

When sketching a graph of a function, you need to plot enough points to understand the general behavior of the new function.

   c. Add the corresponding y-values of $f(x)$ and $g(x)$ on each dashed vertical line to determine points on $m(x)$. Then sketch the graph of $m(x)$. Show or explain your work.

   d. Verify your graph of $m(x)$ using one or more pairs of points that are not key points.

   e. Compare the function you graphed in this question with the prediction you made in Question 1. Describe any errors you may have made in your prediction.

Let's consider operations on different types of graphs. Let's look at a linear function and a constant function.

1. Analyze the graphs of $j(x)$ and $h(x)$.

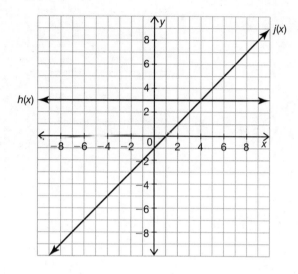

a. Predict the function family of $c(x)$ if $c(x) = j(x) + h(x)$. Then sketch the graph of $c(x)$.

b. Describe the relationship between original functions and $c(x)$. Explain the relationship between the functions in terms of their graphical and algebraic representations.

c. Predict the function family of $n(x)$ if $n(x) = j(x) - h(x)$. Then sketch the graph of $n(x)$.

How will your process of sketching a graph change now that you are subtracting two functions?

d. Describe the relationship between the original functions and $n(x)$. Explain the relationship between the functions in terms of their graphical and algebraic representations.

Now let's look at what happens when you add and subtract the outputs of two parallel lines.

2. Analyze the graphs of $s(x)$ and $v(x)$.

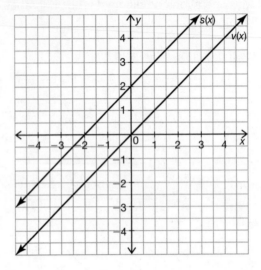

a. Sketch the graph of $w(x) = s(x) + v(x)$.

b. Describe the shape of $w(x)$ compared to $s(x)$ and $v(x)$. Explain why adding the output values changes the shape of the new graph in this way.

Explain your answer in terms of the graphical and the algebraic representations.

c. Sketch the graph of $m(x)$ if $m(x) = s(x) - v(x)$.

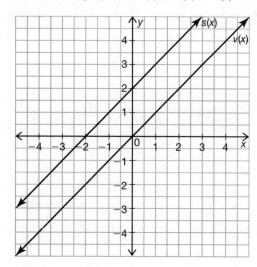

Make a prediction about the new graph before you start!

d. Sketch the graph of $n(x)$ if $n(x) = v(x) - s(x)$.

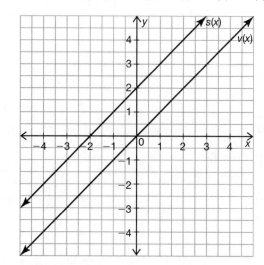

e. Describe the shape of the graph when you subtract $s(x)$ and $v(x)$. Will subtracting the output values of any two parallel lines have this same result? Explain your reasoning.

3. Mrs. Webb asked her students to determine $v(x) - s(x)$. Erik's and Lily's work is shown.

Erik

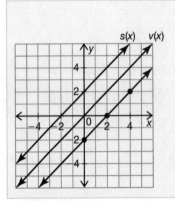

V(x)	t(x)	Differences
0	−2	−2
2	0	−2
4	2	−2

The new graph is located 2 units below $v(x)$. I know this is correct because each point has a difference of −2

Lily

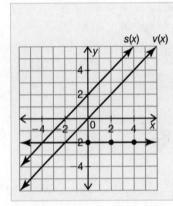

The new graph is located at $y = -2$.
I know this is correct because I subtracted several points and the y-value was always −2.

Who's correct? Explain why one graph is correct and the error made to create the other graph.

Now, let's work backwards.

4. Analyze the graphs of $h(x)$ and $k(x)$.

a. Draw the function $j(x)$ with outputs such that $h(x) + j(x) = k(x)$.

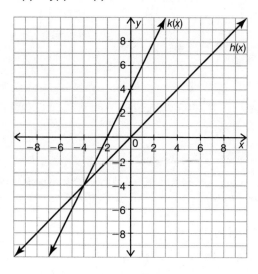

b. Complete the table of values to verify that $h(x) + j(x) = k(x)$.

x	$h(x)$	$j(x)$	$k(x) = h(x) + j(x)$
−2			
−1			
0			
1			
2			

c. Describe examples of the additive inverse and additive identity properties for output values in this problem.

d. Use the graph or table of values to determine the algebraic expressions for $h(x)$, $j(x)$, and $k(x)$. Algebraically show that $h(x) + j(x)$ is equivalent to $k(x)$.

e. How can you determine from the graph, the table of values, and the algebraic expressions that the functions $h(x)$, $j(x)$, and $k(x)$ are all linear?

graph:

table:

equation:

f. Do you think adding two linear functions will always result in another linear function? Explain your reasoning.

So far, you have only considered two linear functions. Now let's explore a linear function and a quadratic function.

5. Analyze the graphs of $k(x)$ and $p(x)$.

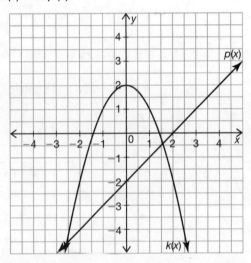

a. Predict the function family of $a(x)$ if $a(x) = k(x) + p(x)$. Explain your prediction.

b. Sketch the graph of function $a(x)$. Show or explain your work.

c. Do you think adding a linear function and a quadratic function will always result in a quadratic function? Explain your reasoning in terms of the algebraic and graphical representations of the functions.

6. Draw the graphs that meet the criteria provided.

a. Sketch the graph of two different functions whose sum is a parabola opening up. What conclusions can you make about the two functions?

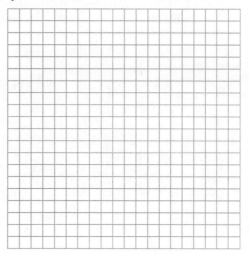

Take some time to experiment with a graphing calculator. Enter the first function as y_1 and the second function as y_2. Graph their sum as $y_3 = y_1 + y_2$. Try to generalize based on what you observe.

b. Sketch the graph of two functions whose sum is the horizontal line $y = 0$. What conclusions can you make about the two functions?

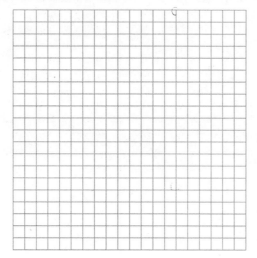

c. Sketch the graph of two functions whose sum is not a function. What conclusions can you make about the two functions?

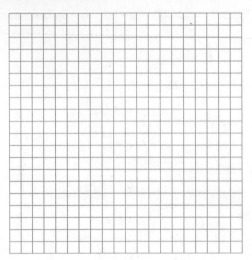

PROBLEM 3   **They're Multiplying!!**

Just as you added and subtracted functions in the previous problems, you can also build functions through multiplication.

1. Analyze the graphs of $f(x)$ and $g(x)$.

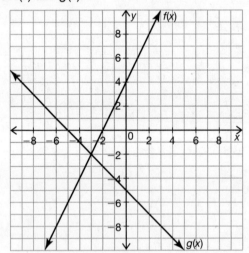

a. Predict the function family of $h(x)$ if $h(x) = f(x) \cdot g(x)$.
Explain your reasoning.

You can use key points when multiplying just like you did when adding and subtracting.

b. Sketch the graph of $h(x)$. Show or explain your work.

c. Describe the differences between the graphs of $f(x)$ and $g(x)$ and the graph of $h(x)$.

d. Was your prediction in part (a) correct? What was the same/different after you multiplied the output values of key points?

2. You can analyze a table of values to determine the graphical behavior of functions.

a. Complete the table of values for $h(x) = f(x) \cdot g(x)$.

x	f(x)	g(x)	h(x)
−7	−10	2	
−6	−8	1	
−5	−6	0	
−4	−4	−1	
−3	−2	−2	
−2	0	−3	
−1	2	−4	
0	4	−5	

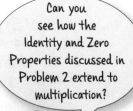

Can you see how the Identity and Zero Properties discussed in Problem 2 extend to multiplication?

b. What patterns do you notice in the table?

c. Analyze the first and second differences for each function. How do you know $f(x)$ and $g(x)$ are linear but $h(x)$ is not?

3. Consider the sign of the output values for each function in the table.

   a. For which input values are the output values of $h(x)$ negative? For which input values are the output values of $h(x)$ positive?

This is just like multiplying real numbers.

   b. How does the sign of the output values of $f(x)$ and $g(x)$ determine the sign of the output values of $h(x)$?

4. Consider the x-intercepts for $f(x)$, $g(x)$ and $h(x)$.

   a. Identify the x-intercepts for each function.

   $f(x)$:

   $g(x)$:

   $h(x)$:

   b. What pattern do you notice in the x-intercepts?

The **Zero Product Property** states that if the product of two or more factors is equal to zero, then at least one factor must be equal to zero.

Remember that the Zero Product Property is important for solving quadratic functions in factored form.

    c. How does the Zero Product Property relate to the x-intercepts of the three functions?

5. Analyze the graphs of $s(x)$ and $v(x)$.

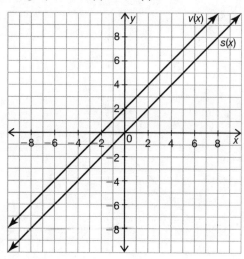

Predict the function family of your sketch before you get started!

a. Sketch the graph of $p(x)$ if $p(x) = s(x) \cdot v(x)$.

b. Identify the x-intercepts of $p(x)$. Explain the relationship between the x-intercepts of $p(x)$ and the x-intercepts of $s(x)$ and $v(x)$.

c. Identify the vertex of $p(x)$. What is the relationship between the vertex of $p(x)$ and the functions $s(x)$ and $v(x)$?

d. In Problem 2 of this lesson, you added the functions $s(x)$ and $v(x)$ to create function $w(x)$. How is multiplication the same? How is it different?

6. Analyze the graphs of $a(x)$ and $b(x)$.

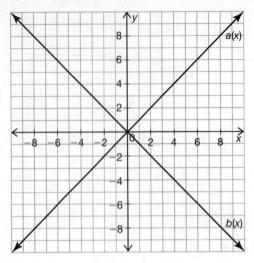

a. Sketch the graph of $c(x)$ if $c(x) = a(x) \cdot b(x)$.

b. Describe the shape of $c(x)$.

7. Analyze the graph of $r(x)$.

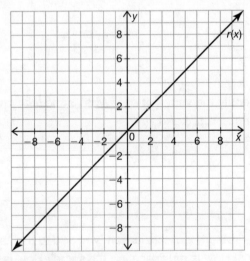

a. Sketch the graph of $d(x)$ if $d(x) = r(x) \cdot r(x)$.

b. Describe the shape of $d(x)$.

8. Analyze the graphs of $f(x)$ and $g(x)$.

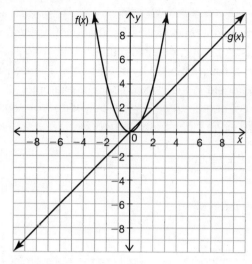

a. Sketch the graph of $m(x)$ if $m(x) = f(x) \cdot g(x)$.

b. Describe the shape of $m(x)$.

c. Do you think multiplying a quadratic function and a linear function will always result in a graph with this shape? Explain your reasoning.

Talk the Talk

While you may not have realized it, the functions you worked with throughout this lesson are *polynomials*. A **polynomial** is a mathematical expression involving the sum of powers in one or more variables multiplied by coefficients. The **degree** of a polynomial is the greatest variable exponent in the expression. For example, $4x^3 + 2x^2 + 5x + 1$ is a polynomial expression of degree three, $2x$ is a polynomial of degree 1, and a constant such as 5 has degree zero since it can be written as $5x^0$.

1. Given the functions,
   - $y_1 = ax^2$,
   - $y_2 = bx$, and
   - $y_3 = c$

   generalize the function family of the polynomial when:

   a. $y_1 + y_2$

   b. $y_1 + y_3$

   c. $y_2 + y_3$

2. When two functions of different degree are added, what can you say about the degree of the resulting function?

> Use a graphing calculator to explore functions of higher degree than 2. What are the shapes of functions with degree 3, 4, and higher? Do they keep this shape when other functions with lower degrees are added to them?

Be prepared to share your solutions and methods.

Chapter 3 Summary

KEY TERMS

- relation (3.3)
- function (3.3)
- function notation (3.3)

- Zero Product Property (3.5)
- polynomial (3.5)
- degree (3.5)

3.1 Identifying Patterns Within a Sequence

Patterns are found throughout nature and our everyday lives. Some patterns can be described numerically.

Example

Draw the next three terms for the pattern shown.

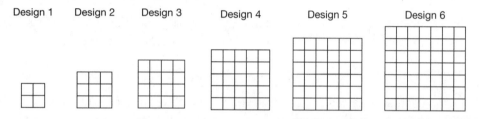

Design 1   Design 2   Design 3   Design 4   Design 5   Design 6

Design 1 is made of 4 small tiles, Design 2 is made of 9 small tiles, and so on. The total number of tiles in each pattern is a perfect square. So, the terms are $2^2 = 4$, $3^2 = 9$, $4^2 = 16$, $5^2 = 25$, $6^2 = 36$, and $7^2 = 49$.

3.1 Using Patterns to Solve Problems

Once you determine a pattern, you can predict the next term in the sequence.

Example

Ji is the coach for a soccer team. He wants to develop a phone tree for communicating with the team. He will call two people and each of those two people will call two more people. This pattern will continue until all team members and coaches have been contacted.

Rounds of Calls	Number of Calls Made	Cumulative Total Number of Calls Made
First round (Ji)	2	2
Second round (two teammates)	4	6
Third round (four teammates)	8	14
Fourth round (eight teammates)	16	30

The number of calls made each day is doubling. So, during the fifth round, $2 \cdot 16 = 32$ calls are made. During the sixth round, $2 \cdot 32 = 64$ calls are made.

3.2 Writing Algebraic Expressions to Describe Patterns

Algebraic expressions can be used when you want to predict patterns or represent real-life scenarios using mathematics.

Example

A website goes live and receives 83 visits in the first day. During the second day, the site receives 91 visits. The third day, the site receives 107 visits. Use an algebraic expression to represent the number of visits the site receives each day.

Day	Number of Visits to the Website
First day	83
Second day	91
Third day	107
Fourth day	139
Fifth day	203

The difference between each term in the pattern is $4(2^1)$ or 8, then $4(2^2)$ or 16, then $4(2^3)$ or 32, and so on. The first term is 8 more than 75. So, an expression to represent the number of visits the site receives each day is $4(2^x) + 75$.

Representing Patterns

Numeric patterns can be represented as expressions, tables, and graphs. After the pattern is graphed on a coordinate plane, the graph can be identified as linear, exponential, quadratic, or none of these.

Example

A salesperson works for four hours. During the first hour, she has 6 clients. During the second hour, she has 8 clients. During the third hour, she has 6 clients. During the fourth hour, she has 0 clients. The table shown represents the number of clients the salesperson has after each hour and also an expression to represent the number of clients the salesperson sees each hour. The graph represents a quadratic model of the data.

Time (hours)	Number of Clients
1	6
2	8
3	6
4	0
n	$-2n^2 + 8n$

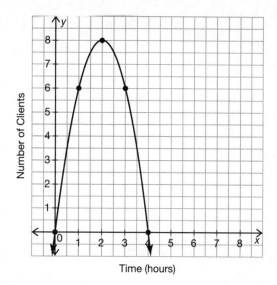

3.3 Identifying Functions

A relation describes how input values are mapped to output values in a pattern. A function is a relation that has only one output for each input. Function notation is a way to represent functions algebraically.

Example

The table and the graph represent relations. Because there is only one output for each input in the relations, they are functions. Because the same outputs are matched to each input, the functions are equivalent.

x	y
−3	25
−2	11
−1	3
0	1
1	5
2	15
3	31

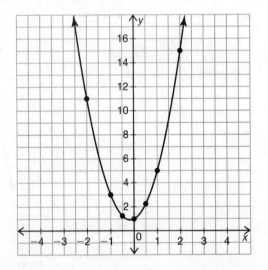

3.3 Modeling Real-World Scenarios

Tables, graphs, and equations can be used to represent real-world scenarios. A table shows the numeric values in columns. A graph shows the relation visually. The graph clearly shows whether the graph is a function or not. An equation uses numbers and variables to model the scenario.

Example

A store is having a sale on smartphones. The store opens at 8:00 AM and has 96 smartphones. After 1 hour, the store has 80 smartphones remaining. After 2 hours, the store has 64 smartphones remaining. If the pattern of sales continues at this rate, at what time will the store run out of smartphones? The number of smartphones in the store can be represented by a table and a graph. Based on the graph, the store will have zero smartphones after 6 hours.

Time	Time Since the Store Opened (hours)	Number of Smartphones Remaining
8:00 AM	0	96
9:00 AM	1	80
10:00 AM	2	64
11:00 AM	3	48
Noon	4	32
1:00 PM	5	16
2:00 PM	6	0

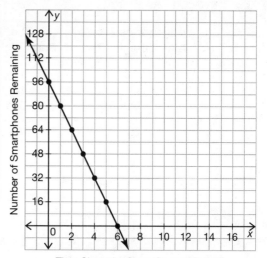

Time Since the Store Opened (hours)

3.4

A table, graph, and equation can be used to represent real-world situations. Any of these forms can be used to analyze the situation.

Example

The cost of a party can be calculated by multiplying the number of people attending by 15 and then adding 24. An equation to model the situation is $y = 15x + 24$. The table lists the cost for specific numbers of people attending. The graph of the function is also shown. Based on the graph, the cost of the party will keep increasing as the number of people attending the party increases. Based on the table, for every 10 additional people attending the party, the cost of the party increases by $150.

Number of People Attending the Party	Cost of the Party (dollars)
10	174
20	324
30	474
40	624
50	774

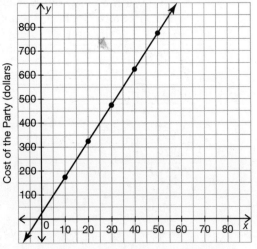

Number of People Attending the Party

Using a Graph and Function to Analyze Problems

The table or graph for a situation can provide valuable information about the scenario. The minimum or maximum of a quadratic equation can provide context for the situation or aid in predicting or analyzing the scenario.

Example

Larissa is running a car wash as a fundraiser for her school. In the first hour, the group earns $12 in donations for car washes. The amount of money earned each hour is listed in the table and shown in the graph. The group earns a maximum of $28 in the third hour of the car wash.

Time Since the Car Wash Started (hours)	Amount of Money Earned Each Hour (dollars)
1	12
2	23
3	28
4	27
5	20
6	7

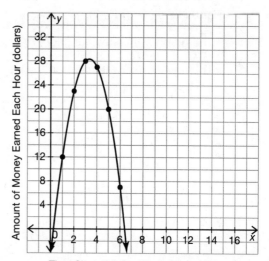

To add or subtract two functions graphically, first identify several key points. Some key points include intersection points, x-intercepts, and y-intercepts. For each input value, add or subtract the output values for each function to calculate the output value of the new function. Then draw the graph of the new function.

Example

Add $g(x) = x + 2$ and $f(x) = 2x - 6$ graphically.

Use the key points $(-2, 0)$, $(-2, -10)$, $(0, 2)$, $(0, -6)$, $(3, 0)$, and $(3, 5)$.

The new function contains the points $(-2, 0 - 10)$ or $(-2, -10)$, $(0, 2 - 6)$ or $(0, -4)$, and $(3, 0 + 5)$ or $(3, 5)$.

The graph of the new function, $m(x)$ is shown.

The equation for the function $m(x)$ is $m(x) = 3x - 4$.

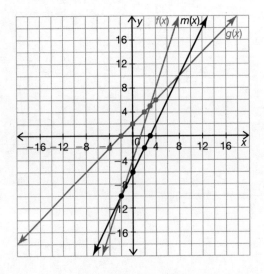

Multiplying Functions Graphically

To multiply two functions graphically, first identify several key points. Some key points include intersection points, *x*-intercepts, and *y*-intercepts. For each input value, multiply the output values for each function to calculate the output value of the new function. Then draw the graph of the new function.

Example

Multiply $j(x) = x + 3$ and $k(x) = 2x - 1$ to determine $f(x)$.

Use a table of values to graph the functions.

x	$j(x) = x + 3$	$k(x) = 2x - 1$	$f(x)$
−3	0	−7	0
−2	1	−5	−5
−1	2	−3	−6
0	3	−1	−3
1	4	1	4
2	5	3	15
3	6	5	30

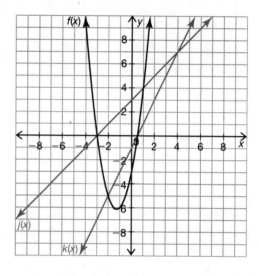

Quadratic Functions

> The Millennium Bridge in London is a bridge solely for pedestrians. It was opened in June of 2000—hence its name—but was closed for 2 years for repairs after it got the nickname "Wobbly Bridge."

Shape and Structure
Forms of Quadratic Functions

LEARNING GOALS

In this lesson, you will:

- Match a quadratic function with its corresponding graph.
- Identify key characteristics of quadratic functions based on the form of the function.
- Analyze the different forms of quadratic functions.
- Use key characteristics of specific forms of quadratic functions to write equations.
- Write quadratic functions to represent problem situations.

KEY TERMS

- standard form of a quadratic function
- factored form of a quadratic function
- vertex form of a quadratic function
- concavity of a parabola

Have you ever seen a tightrope walker? If you've ever seen this, you know that it is quite amazing to witness a person able to walk on a thin piece of rope. However, since safety is always a concern, there is usually a net just in case of a fall.

That brings us to a young French daredevil named Phillippe Petit. Back in 1974 with the help of some friends, he spent all night secretly placing a 450 pound cable between the World Trade Center Towers in New York City. At dawn, to the shock and amazement of onlookers, the fatigued 24-year old Petit stepped out onto the wire. Ignoring the frantic calls of the police, he walked, jumped, laughed, and even performed a dance routine on the wire for nearly an hour without a safety net! Mr. Petit was of course arrested upon climbing back to the safety of the ledge. When asked why he performed such an unwise, dangerous act, Phillippe said: "When I see three oranges, I juggle; when I see two towers, I walk."

You can see the events unfold in the 2002 Academy Award winning documentary Man on Wire by James Marsh.

Have you ever challenged yourself to do something difficult just to see if you could do it?

It's All in the Form

1. Cut out each quadratic function and graph on the next page two pages.

   a. Tape each quadratic function to its corresponding graph.

Please do not use graphing calculators for this activity. What information can you tell from looking at the function and what can you tell by looking at each graph?

   b. Explain the method(s) you used to match the functions with their graphs.

a. $f(x) = 2(x + 1)(x + 5)$

d. $f(x) = (x - 1)^2$

g. $f(x) = -(x + 4)^2 - 2$

b. $f(x) = \frac{1}{3}x^2 + \pi x + 6.4$

e. $f(x) = 2(x - 1)(x - 5)$

h. $f(x) = -5x^2 - x + 21$

c. $f(x) = -2.5(x - 3)(x - 3)$

f. $f(x) = x^2 + 12x - 1$

i. $f(x) = -(x + 2)^2 - 4$

4

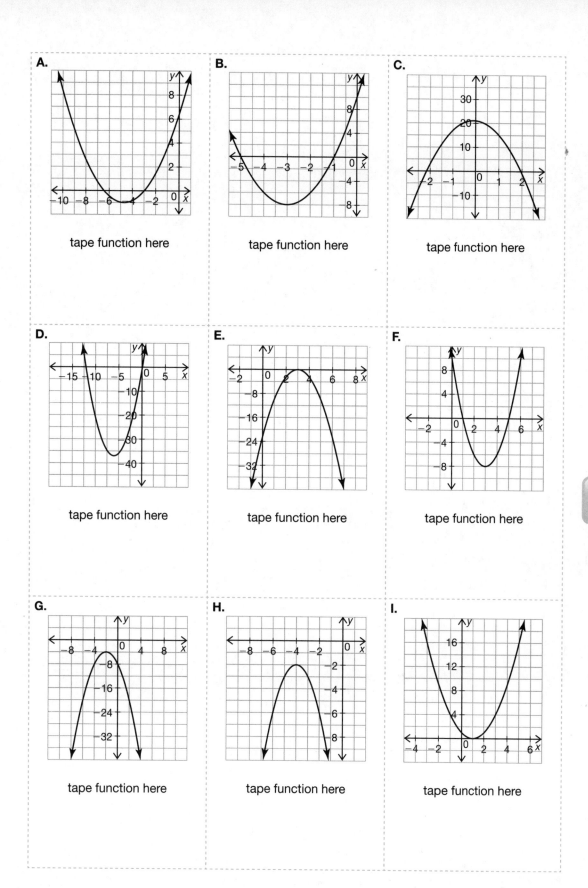

A.

tape function here

B.

tape function here

C.

tape function here

D.

tape function here

E.

tape function here

F.

tape function here

G.

tape function here

H.

tape function here

I.

tape function here

4

Recall that quadratic functions can be written in different forms.

- **standard form:** $f(x) = ax^2 + bx + c$, where a does not equal 0.
- **factored form:** $f(x) = a(x - r_1)(x - r_2)$, where a does not equal 0.
- **vertex form:** $f(x) = a(x - h)^2 + k$, where a does not equal 0.

2. Sort your graphs with matching equations into 3 piles based on the function form.

Keep these piles; you will use them again at the end of this Problem.

The graphs of quadratic functions can be described using key characteristics:

- x-intercept(s),
- y-intercept,
- vertex,
- axis of symmetry, and
- concave up or down.

Concavity of a parabola describes whether a parabola opens up or opens down. A parabola is concave down if it opens downward; a parabola is concave up if it opens upward.

3. The form of a quadratic function highlights different key characteristics. State the characteristics you can determine from each.

- standard form

- factored form

- vertex form

4. Christine and Kate were asked to determine the vertex of two different quadratic functions each written in different forms. Analyze their calculations.

 Christine

$f(x) = 2x^2 + 12x + 10$

The quadratic function is in standard form. So I know the axis of symmetry is $x = \frac{-b}{2a}$.

$$x = \frac{-12}{2(2)}$$
$$= -3.$$

Now that I know the axis of symmetry, I can substitute that value into the function to determine the y-coordinate of the vertex.

$$f(-3) = 2(-3)^2 + 12(-3) + 10$$
$$= 2(9) - 36 + 10$$
$$= 18 - 36 + 10$$
$$= 8$$

Therefore, the vertex is $(-3, 8)$.

 Kate

$g(x) = \frac{1}{2}(x + 3)(x - 7)$

The form of the function tells me the x-intercepts are -3 and 7. I also know the x-coordinate of the vertex will be directly in the middle of the x-intercepts. So, all I have to do is calculate the average.

$$x = \frac{-3 + 7}{2}$$
$$= \frac{4}{2} = 2$$

Now that I know the x-coordinate of the vertex, I can substitute that value into the function to determine the y-coordinate.

$$g(2) = \frac{1}{2}(2 + 3)(2 - 7)$$
$$= \frac{1}{2}(5)(-5)$$
$$= -12.5$$

Therefore, the vertex is $(2, -12.5)$.

a. How are these methods similar? How are they different?

b. What must Kate do to use Christine's method?

c. What must Christine do to use Kate's method?

5. Analyze each table on the following three pages. Paste each function and its corresponding graph from Question 2 in the "Graphs and Their Functions" section of the appropriate table. Then, explain how you can determine each key characteristic based on the form of the given function.

Standard Form $f(x) = ax^2 + bx + c$, where $a \neq 0$
Graphs and Their Functions

Methods to Identify and Determine Key Characteristics		
Axis of Symmetry	**x-intercept(s)**	**Concavity**

Vertex	**y-intercept**

Factored Form
$f(x) = a(x - r_1)(x - r_2)$, where $a \neq 0$

Graphs and Their Functions

Methods to Identify and Determine Key Characteristics

Axis of Symmetry	x-intercept(s)	Concavity

Vertex	y-intercept

Vertex Form
$f(x) = a(x - h)^2 + k$, where $a \neq 0$

Graphs and Their Functions

Methods to Identify and Determine Key Characteristics

Axis of Symmetry	x-intercept(s)	Concavity

Vertex	y-intercept

1. Analyze each graph. Then, circle the function(s) which could model the graph. Describe the reasoning you used to either eliminate or choose each function.

a.

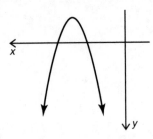

$$f_1(x) = -2(x + 1)(x + 4) \qquad f_2(x) = -\frac{1}{3}x^2 - 3x - 6 \qquad f_3(x) = 2(x + 1)(x + 4)$$

$$f_4(x) = 2x^2 - 8.9 \qquad f_5(x) = 2(x - 1)(x - 4) \qquad f_6(x) = -(x - 6)^2 + 3$$

$$f_7(x) = -3(x + 2)(x - 3) \qquad f_8(x) = -(x + 6)^2 + 3$$

Think about the information given by each function and the relative position of the graph.

b.

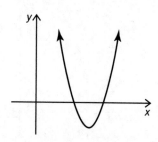

$$f_1(x) = 2(x - 75)^2 - 92 \qquad f_2(x) = (x - 8)(x + 2) \qquad f_3(x) = 8x^2 - 88x + 240$$

$$f_4(x) = -3(x - 1)(x - 5) \qquad f_5(x) = -2(x - 75)^2 - 92 \qquad f_6(x) = x^2 + 6x - 2$$

$$f_7(x) = 2(x + 4)^2 - 2 \qquad f_8(x) = (x + 1)(x + 3)$$

c.

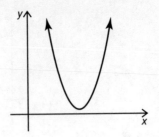

$f_1(x) = 3(x + 1)(x - 5)$ $f_2(x) = 2(x + 6)^2 - 5$ $f_3(x) = 4x^2 - 400x + 10{,}010$

$f_4(x) = 3(x + 1)(x + 5)$ $f_5(x) = 2(x - 6)^2 + 5$ $f_6(x) = x^2 + 2x - 5$

2. Consider the two functions shown from Question 1. Identify the form of the function given, and then write the function in the other two forms, if possible. If it is not possible, explain why.

a. From part (a): $f_1(x) = -2(x + 1)(x + 4)$

b. From part (c): $f_5(x) = 2(x - 6)^2 + 5$

1. George and Pat were each asked to write a quadratic equation with a vertex of (4, 8). Analyze each student's work. Describe the similarities and differences in their equations and determine who is correct.

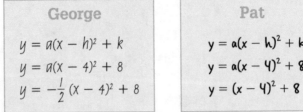

George	Pat
$y = a(x - h)^2 + k$	$y = a(x - h)^2 + k$
$y = a(x - 4)^2 + 8$	$y = a(x - 4)^2 + 8$
$y = -\frac{1}{2}(x - 4)^2 + 8$	$y = (x - 4)^2 + 8$

2. Consider the 3 forms of quadratic functions and state the number of unknown values in each.

Form	Number of Unknown Values
$f(x) = a(x - h)^2 + k$	
$f(x) = a(x - r_1)(x - r_2)$	
$f(x) = ax^2 + bx + c$	

a. If a function is written in vertex form and you know the vertex, what is still unknown?

b. If a function is written in factored form and you know the roots, what is still unknown?

c. If a function is written in any form and you know one point, what is still unknown? State the unknown values for each form of a quadratic function.

d. If you only know the vertex, what more do you need to write a unique function? Explain your reasoning.

e. If you only know the roots, what more do you need to write a unique function? Explain your reasoning.

You can write a unique quadratic function given a vertex and a point on the parabola.

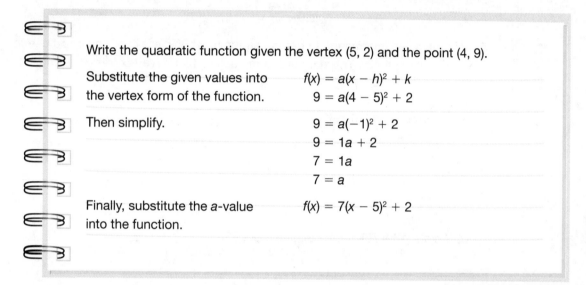

Write the quadratic function given the vertex (5, 2) and the point (4, 9).

Substitute the given values into the vertex form of the function.	$f(x) = a(x - h)^2 + k$ $9 = a(4 - 5)^2 + 2$
Then simplify.	$9 = a(-1)^2 + 2$ $9 = 1a + 2$ $7 = 1a$ $7 = a$
Finally, substitute the a-value into the function.	$f(x) = 7(x - 5)^2 + 2$

You can write a unique quadratic function given the roots and a point on the parabola.

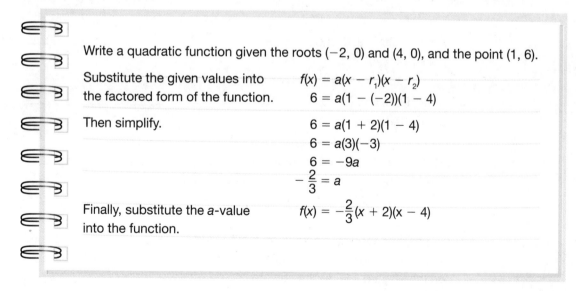

Write a quadratic function given the roots (−2, 0) and (4, 0), and the point (1, 6).

Substitute the given values into the factored form of the function.	$f(x) = a(x - r_1)(x - r_2)$ $6 = a(1 - (-2))(1 - 4)$
Then simplify.	$6 = a(1 + 2)(1 - 4)$ $6 = a(3)(-3)$ $6 = -9a$ $-\dfrac{2}{3} = a$
Finally, substitute the a-value into the function.	$f(x) = -\dfrac{2}{3}(x + 2)(x - 4)$

3. Explain why knowing the vertex and a point creates a unique quadratic function.

4. If you are given the roots, how many unique quadratic functions can you write? Explain your reasoning.

5. Use the given information to determine the most efficient form you could use to write the function. Write standard form, factored form, vertex form, or none in the space provided.

a. minimum point (6, −75)
y-intercept (0, 15)

_____

b. points (2, 0), (8, 0), and (4, 6)

_____

c. points (100, 75), (450, 75), and (150, 95)

_____

d. points (3, 3), (4, 3), and (5, 3)

_____

e. x-intercepts: (7.9, 0) and (−7.9, 0)
point (−4, −4)

_____

f. roots: (3, 0) and (12, 0)
point (10, 2)

_____

g. Max hits a baseball off a tee that is 3 feet high. The ball reaches a maximum height of 20 feet when it is 15 feet from the tee.

_____

h. A grasshopper was standing on the 35 yard line of a football field. He jumped, and landed on the 38 yard line. At the 36 yard line he was 8 inches in the air.

_____

PROBLEM 4   Just Another Day at the Circus

Write a quadratic function to represent each situation using the given information. Be sure to define your variables.

1. The Amazing Larry is a human cannonball. He would like to reach a maximum height of 30 feet during his next launch. Based on Amazing Larry's previous launches, his assistant DaJuan has estimated that this will occur when he is 40 feet from the cannon. When Amazing Larry is shot from the cannon, he is 10 feet above the ground. Write a function to represent Amazing Larry's height in terms of his distance.

2. Crazy Cornelius is a fire jumper. He is attempting to run and jump through a ring of fire. He runs for 10 feet. Then, he begins his jump just 4 feet from the fire and lands on the other side 3 feet from the fire ring. When Cornelius was 1 foot from the fire ring at the beginning of his jump, he was 3.5 feet in the air. Write a function to represent Crazy Cornelius' height in terms of his distance. Round to the nearest hundredth.

Remember, the general equation to represent height over time is $h(t) = -16t^2 + v_0 t + h_0$ where v_0 is the initial velocity in feet per second and h_0 is the initial height in feet.

3. Harsh Knarsh is attempting to jump across an alligator filled swamp. She takes off from a ramp 30 feet high with a speed of 95 feet per second. Write a function to represent Harsh Knarsh's height in terms of time.

 Be prepared to share your solutions and methods.

Function Sense
Translating Functions

LEARNING GOALS

In this lesson, you will:

- Analyze the basic form of a quadratic function.
- Identify the reference points of the basic form of a quadratic function.
- Understand the structure of the basic quadratic function.
- Graph quadratic functions through transformations.
- Identify the effect on a graph by replacing $f(x)$ by $f(x - C) + D$.
- Identify transformations given equations of quadratic functions.
- Write quadratic functions given a graph.

KEY TERMS

- reference points
- transformation
- rigid motion
- argument of a function
- translation

Have you ever taken a road trip? For most American children, some road trips were the bane of existence—especially with annoying siblings. Of course, on the drive back, kids might get excited by a point of reference such as a road sign indicating the number of miles remaining before getting home, or seeing a landscape that is comfortably familiar. Adults commonly use reference points on road trips as well. Most U.S. national map books give estimated hours of travel and distances between key cities across the country. These help motorists and truckers determine if they should continue on, or get off the highway for a bit of shut eye.

What types of reference points have you used? How did you use those reference points?

It All Comes Down to the Basics

So far in this course, all the different forms of quadratic functions you have studied have been based on the function $f(x) = x^2$. This function is the basic form of a quadratic function. From the form of this function, you know the vertex is (0,0).

The pattern of this function is that for every input value, x, the output value, $f(x)$, is squared.

1. Let's consider the structure of $f(x) = x^2$ and its corresponding graph.

 a. Complete the table. Then plot and label the points on the coordinate plane.

x	$f(x) = x^2$
0	
1	
2	

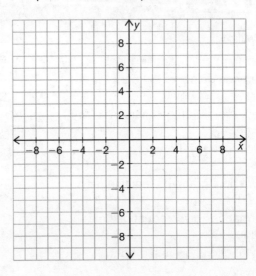

 b. Draw a dashed line to represent the axis of symmetry. Then plot and label all symmetric points. Finally, draw a smooth curve to represent $f(x) = x^2$.

You just analyzed the basic form of a quadratic function, $f(x) = x^2$. For a quadratic function, if you know the vertex and any two points to the right of that vertex, you can use the axis of symmetry to identify the other half of the parabola. A set of key points that help identify the basic form of any function are called **reference points**. The reference points of the basic quadratic function are defined in the table shown.

Reference Points of the Basic Quadratic Function	
P	(0, 0)
Q	(1, 1)
R	(2, 4)

So, for quadratics I just need to remember the relationship between the vertex and two points. To plot Q, I go to the right 1 and up 1 from the vertex, and to plot point R, I go to the right 2 and up 4 from the vertex.

Now that you understand the structure of the basic quadratic function, let's explore how to apply *transformations* to graph new functions. Recall that a **transformation** is the mapping, or movement, of all the points of a figure in a plane according to a common operation. Translations, reflections, rotations, and dilations are examples of transformations. In previous courses, you studied the effects that transformations had on graphs of functions and various figures on the coordinate plane. A **rigid motion** is a transformation that preserves size and shape.

1. Identify which transformations are rigid motions that preserve size and shape.

Previously, you worked with the vertex form of quadratic functions, $f(x) = a(x - h)^2 + k$, which represent transformations of $f(x) = x^2$.

2. Given a quadratic function written in vertex form, $f(x) = a(x - h)^2 + k$, identify the effect the h- and k-values have on the graph of the basic quadratic function.

Which transformations are represented by the h- and k-values?

Vertex form is a specific form of a quadratic function. In this lesson, you will use the basic quadratic function to explore various function transformations. Eventually, you will learn how to generalize about transformations performed across many different function types, but first let's establish a form that will be representative of any function. Transformations performed on any function $f(x)$ to form a new function $g(x)$ can be described by the transformational function form:

$$g(x) = Af(B(x - C)) + D$$

where A, B, C, and D represent different constants.

Let's make some connections and compare the vertex form of a quadratic function, $f(x) = a(x - h)^2 + k$, to the transformational function form $g(x) = Af(B(x - C)) + D$, where $B = 1$.

3. How are the h- and k-values of the vertex form of the quadratic function represented in the transformational function form?

4

The goal is to understand the effects of transformations using a general function form, and then being able to apply that knowledge to any function family.

Cool! I can learn something once and apply it over and over again to any function type.

Let's consider the constants C and D, where A and B both equal 1 and the effects each value has on the graph of the basic quadratic function. Let A and B both equal 1.

$$\text{Given } f(x) = x^2$$

$$\text{Graph } g(x) = f(x - 4) + 2$$

In the function $g(x)$, $C = 4$ and $D = 2$. The C-value and the D-value will tell you how to translate the function. Notice, the value of 4 is on the *inside* of the function, or the *argument of the function*. The **argument of a function** is the variable, term, or expression on which the function operates. The value 2 is on the *outside* of the function. Recall values on the inside of a function affect the x-values of the function, and values on the outside affect y-values of the function. So, the C-value will tell you how many units to translate the function left or right, and the D-value will tell you how many units to translate the function up or down.

> Remember, translations preserve the same size and shape of the function.

Given $f(x) = x^2$

Graph $g(x) = f(x - 4) + 2$

You can use reference points for $f(x)$ and your knowledge about transformations to graph the function $g(x)$.

From $g(x)$, you know that $C = 4$ and $D = 2$ which tells you the entire graph will translate 4 units to the right and 2 units up.

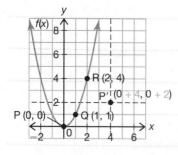 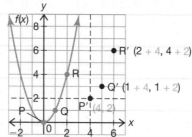 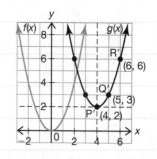

The function $f(x)$ is shown with its reference points. To begin to graph $g(x)$, plot the new vertex, (C, D). This point establishes the new set of axes.

Next, think about the pattern of the basic quadratic function. To plot point Q′, move right 1 unit, and up 1 unit from the vertex. To plot point R′, move right 2 units, and up 4 units from the vertex.

Finally, use symmetry to complete the graph.

> You can think of the vertex of the transformed function as the "origin" of a new set of axes.

4. Analyze the worked example.

   a. Complete the table of values to verify the graph.

Reference Points of Basic Quadratic Function		→	Apply the Transformations	Corresponding Points on g(x)	
P	(0, 0)	→	(0 + ____ , 0 + ____)	P'	(4, 2)
Q	(1, 1)	→	(1 + ____ , 1 + ____)	Q'	(5, 3)
R	(2, 4)	→	(2 + ____ , 4 + ____)	R'	(6, 6)

   b. Why is it important to establish a new set of axes?

   c. Use C and D to write the equations that correspond to the new set of axes.

   d. Name the two points symmetric to Q' and R'.

   e. The function $g(x) = f(x - 4) + 2$ is written in terms of $f(x)$. Rewrite $g(x)$ in terms of x by substituting $(x - 4)$ for x into $f(x)$, and adding 2 onto $f(x)$.

5. Given $f(x) = x^2$, graph $h(x) = f(x - 2)$.

   a. Identify the C- and D-values.

Based on the form of $h(x)$, what do you think the graph will look like?

   b. Complete the table.

Reference Points on $f(x)$	→	Corresponding Points on $h(x)$
(0, 0)	→	
(1, 1)	→	
(2, 4)	→	

   c. Graph $h(x)$ in the same 3 steps as the worked example. Provide the rationale you used below each graph.

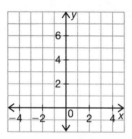 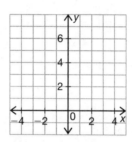 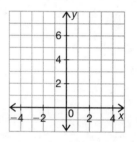

4

6. Given $f(x) = x^2$, graph the function $m(x) = f(x + 2) - 3$.

Reference Points on $f(x)$	$\rightarrow$	Corresponding Points on $m(x)$
(0, 0)	$\rightarrow$	
(1, 1)	$\rightarrow$	
(2, 4)	$\rightarrow$	

What does the form of $m(x)$ tell you?

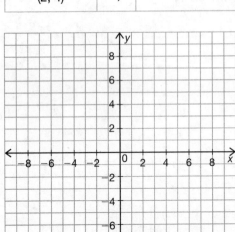

7. Analyze the graphs of $p(x)$ and $m(x)$.

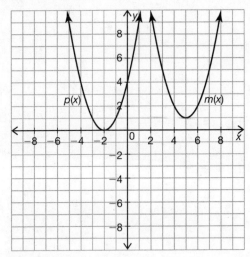

a. If $f(x) = x^2$, write $m(x)$ in terms of $f(x) = x^2$.

b. If $f(x) = x^2$, write $p(x)$ in terms of $f(x) = x^2$.

c. Write $p(x)$ in terms of $m(x)$.

d. Write $m(x)$ in terms of $p(x)$.

A **translation** is a type of transformation that shifts an entire figure or graph the same distance and direction.

Compared with the graph of $y = f(x)$, the graph of $y = f(x - C) + D$:

- shifts left C units if $C < 0$.

- shifts right C units if $C > 0$.

- shifts down D units if $D < 0$.

- shifts up D units if $D > 0$.

8. Given $y = f(x)$, write the coordinate notation represented in $y = f(x - C) + D$.

$(x, y) \rightarrow$ _____

 Be prepared to share your solutions and methods.

4

Up and Down
Vertical Dilations of Quadratic Functions

LEARNING GOALS

In this lesson, you will:

- Graph quadratic functions through vertical dilations.
- Identify the effect on a graph by replacing f(x) by Af(x).
- Write quadratic functions given a graph.

KEY TERMS

- vertical dilation
- vertical stretching
- vertical compression
- reflection
- line of reflection

Have you ever heard that people shrink as they get older? Shrinking can occur from a number of reasons like osteoporosis, or because of the spine compressing over time. What you might not know is that everybody shrinks, and everybody also stretches every single day! This stretching and shrinking occurs because of little discs in a person's spine. They are filled with water, acting as the body's shock absorbers. As the day passes, these little discs lose water, compressing the spine. Then during sleep, the water is replenished, and the spine stretches back to its original size.

Although elderly people do "shrink," and although people expand and contract on a daily basis, people have actually been getting taller. One proof of this observation is the height of doorways in 18th century homes—they were not very tall! This is because people were on average, shorter than today. Over the last 150 years, the average height of a person has increased by 4 inches.

Does this mean that 300 years from now people will be an average of 8 inches taller than what most people are now? Do you think that the average height will eventually reach 9 or 10 feet? Are we destined to become giants, or do you think that this trend will stop?

PROBLEM 1 Vertical Stretching and Compressing

Now, let's explore the effects of the A-value in the transformational function.

$$g(x) = Af(B(x - C)) + D$$

1. Analyze the transformational function. Where is the A-value positioned in terms of the function f: inside or outside the function? Based on the position of the A-value, do you think it will affect the x-values or the y-values? Explain your reasoning.

Let's consider various A-values to understand the effects on the basic function $f(x) = x^2$.

2. Use a graphing calculator to graph each quadratic function with $A > 0$. Sketch and label the graphs.

a.

$A \geq 1$
$2x^2$
$3x^2$
$4x^2$

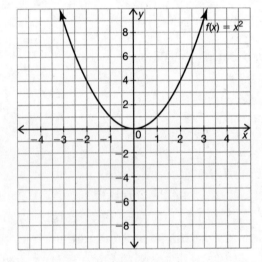

b.

$0 < A < 1$
$\frac{1}{4}x^2$
$\frac{1}{2}x^2$
$\frac{3}{4}x^2$

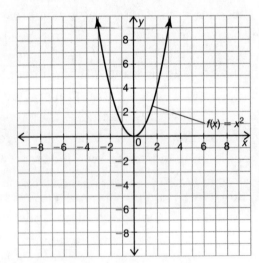

c. Consider the different A-values. How do the graphs in part (a) compare to those in part (b)?

d. Does the A-value affect the x-values or y-values? Explain your reasoning.

A **vertical dilation** is a type of transformation that stretches or compresses an entire figure or graph. In a vertical dilation, notice that the y-coordinate of every point on the graph of a function is multiplied by a common factor, A. You can also think about this as either a vertical stretch or vertical compression. **Vertical stretching** is the stretching of the graph away from the x-axis. **Vertical compression** is the squeezing of a graph towards the x-axis.

3. Is a dilation the type of transformation that preserves both the size and shape of a function? Explain your reasoning.

4. Consider the function $f(x) = \frac{3}{2}x^2$.

Dan says that the graph of this function will look more compressed than the graph of $f(x) = x^2$ because the A-value is a fraction. Jeannie says that the graph of this function will look more stretched because the A-value is greater than 1.
Who is correct? Explain your reasoning.

5. Choose a term that identifies the effect on the graph of replacing $f(x)$ with $Af(x)$:

vertical stretch	vertical compression

a. $A \geq 1$ _____

b. $0 < A < 1$ _____

6. Given the basic function $f(x) = x^2$, use a graphing calculator to graph each quadratic function with $A < 0$. Sketch and label the graphs. Also, use the TABLE feature and analyze each table of values.

a.

$A \le -1$
$-2x^2$
$-3x^2$
$-4x^2$

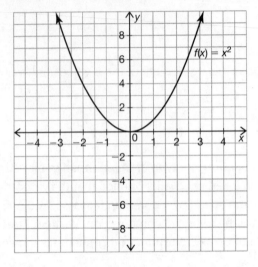

b.

$-1 < A < 0$
$-\dfrac{1}{4}x^2$
$-\dfrac{1}{2}x^2$
$-\dfrac{3}{4}x^2$

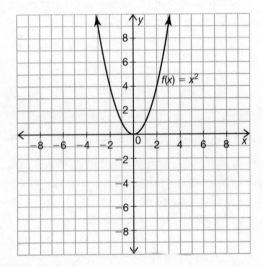

c. How did $A < 0$ affect the graph of the basic function.

d. How do the graphs in part (a) compare to the graphs in Question 2, part (a)?

e. How do the graphs in part (b) compare to the graphs in Question 2, part (b)?

A **reflection** of a graph is a mirror image of a graph across its *line of reflection*. A **line of reflection** is the line that a graph is reflected across.

7. Identify the line of reflection for each graph in Question 6.

Compared with the graph of $y = f(x)$, the graph of $y = Af(x)$ is:

- vertically stretched by a factor of $|A|$ if $|A| > 1$.

- vertically compressed by a factor of $|A|$ if $0 < |A| < 1$.

If $A < 0$, then the graph is also reflected across the x-axis.

 8. Given $y = f(x)$, write the coordinate notation represented in $y = Af(x - C) + D$.

$(x, y) \rightarrow$ _____

9. Use a graphing calculator to sketch each set of equations on the same coordinate plane.

a. $y_1 = x^2 + 2$
$y_2 = -x^2 + 2$

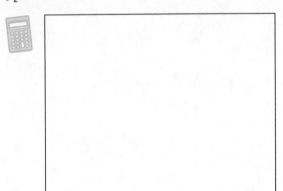

How do the graphs of y_1 and y_2 compare?

b. $y_1 = x^2 + 2$
$y_3 = -y_1$

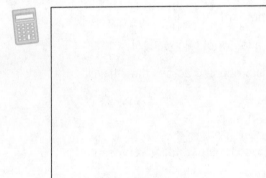

How do the graphs of y_1 and y_3 compare?

10. Explain the differences between the lines of reflections used to produce y_2 and y_3 in Question 9.

Think about where the negative is positioned within the equation and how that affects your decision about applying the reflection.

11. Christian, Julia, and Emily each sketched a graph of the equation $y = -x^2 - 3$ using different strategies. Provide the step-by-step reasoning used by each student.

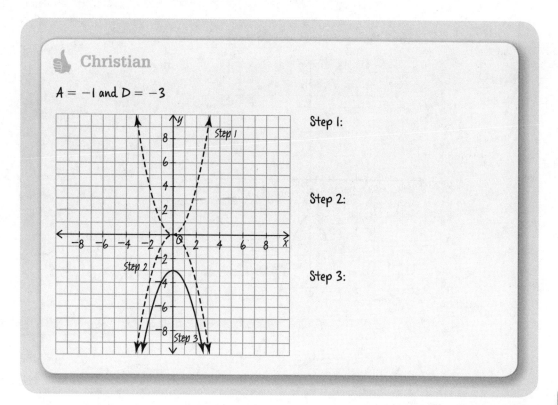

Christian

$A = -1$ and $D = -3$

Step 1:

Step 2:

Step 3:

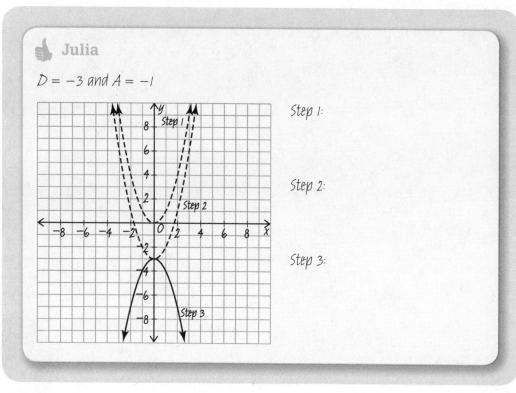

Julia

$D = -3$ and $A = -1$

Step 1:

Step 2:

Step 3:

Emily

I rewrote the equation as $y = -(x^2 + 3)$.

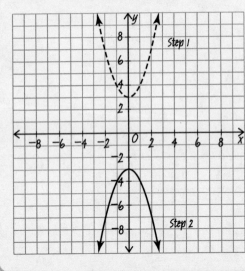

Step 1:

Step 2:

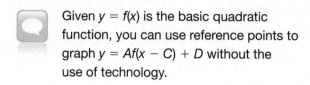

Given $y = f(x)$ is the basic quadratic function, you can use reference points to graph $y = Af(x − C) + D$ without the use of technology.

Think about the pattern of the basic quadratic function and the A-value.

Given $f(x) = x^2$

Graph the function $g(x) = 2f(x − 3) + 4$

You can use reference points for $f(x)$ and your knowledge about transformations to graph the function $g(x)$.

From $g(x)$, you know that $A = 2$, $C = 3$, and $D = 4$.

The vertex for $g(x)$ will be at (3, 4). Notice $A > 0$, so the graph of the function will vertically stretch by a factor of 2.

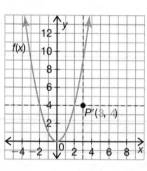

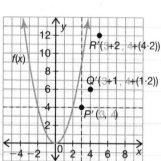

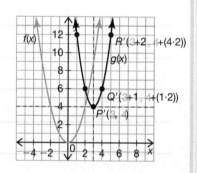

First, plot the new vertex, (C, D). This point establishes the new set of axes.	Next, think about the reference points for the basic quadratic function and that $A = 2$.	Finally, use symmetry to complete the graph.
	To plot point Q' move right 1 unit and up, not 1, but 1×2 units from the vertex P' because all y-coordinates are being multiplied by a factor of 2. To plot point R' move right 2 units from the P' and up, not 4, but 4×2 units.	

12. Analyze the worked example.

   a. Use coordinate notation to represent how the A-, C-, and D-values transform the basic quadratic function to generate $g(x) = 2f(x - 3) + 4$.

      $(x, y) \rightarrow$ _____

   b. Use the coordinate notation from part (a) to complete the table of values to verify the graph.

Reference Points of Basic Quadratic Function	$\rightarrow$	Corresponding Points on $g(x)$
(0, 0)	$\rightarrow$	
(1, 1)	$\rightarrow$	
(2, 4)	$\rightarrow$	

   c. Rewrite $g(x)$ in terms of x.

13. Suppose function $d(x)$ has the same C- and D-values the function $g(x)$ in the worked example, but its A-value is $\frac{1}{2}$.

a. Write $d(x)$ in terms of $f(x)$.

b. How would the graph of $d(x)$ compare to the graph of $g(x)$? Explain your reasoning.

c. Complete the table of values.

Reference Points of Basic Quadratic Function	→	Corresponding Points on $d(x)$
(x, y)	→	
$(0, 0)$	→	
$(1, 1)$	→	
$(2, 4)$	→	

d. Sketch the graph of $d(x)$.

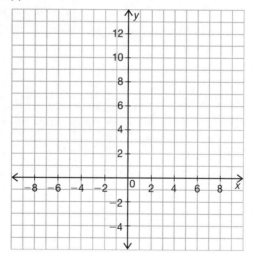

e. Rewrite $d(x)$ in terms of x.

14. Suppose a function, $r(x)$, has the same C- and D-values the function $g(x)$ in the worked example, but its A-value is -2.

a. Write $r(x)$ in terms of $f(x)$.

b. How would the graph of $r(x)$ compare to the graph of $g(x)$? Explain your reasoning.

c. Complete the table of values.

Reference Points of Basic Quadratic Function	→	Corresponding Points on $r(x)$
(x, y)	→	
$(0, 0)$	→	
$(1, 1)$	→	
$(2, 4)$	→	

d. Sketch the graph of $r(x)$.

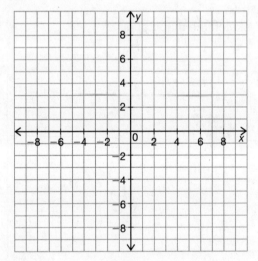

e. Rewrite $r(x)$ in terms of x.

15. Given the graph of $g(x) = 2(x - 3)^2 + 4$ from the worked example.

(graph showing parabola $g(x)$ with vertex at (3, 4))

a. Graph $m(x) = -g(x)$.

b. How is the graph of $m(x)$ the same or different from the graph of $r(x)$ in Question 14?

c. Rewrite $m(x)$ in terms of x.

16. Graph $f(x) = \frac{1}{2}(x - 1)^2 + 3$.

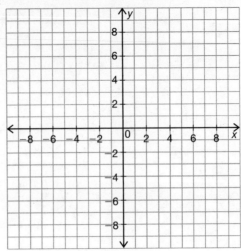

17. Write the functions that represent each graph.

a.

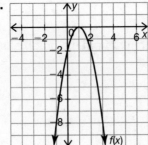

b.

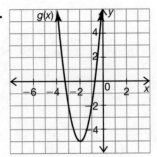

$f(x) =$ _____

$g(x) =$ _____

Be prepared to share your solutions and methods.

Side to Side
Horizontal Dilations of Quadratic Functions

In this lesson, you will:

- Graph quadratic functions through horizontal dilations.
- Identify the effect on a graph by replacing $f(x)$ by $f(Bx)$.
- Write quadratic functions given a graph.

- horizontal dilation
- horizontal stretching
- horizontal compression

Smile for the camera! FLASH! One of the most uncomfortable things about taking a picture indoors is using a flash. And if the picture-taker didn't quite get the shot, it is a double dose of bright lights! Flashes routinely do a number on your eyes—so does the sun. Even though your eyes routinely dilate depending on the light conditions, the sudden flash of light can be uncomfortable for most people. Of course, other things can make your eyes dilate. For example, if you are hungry and you see a commercial for a tantalizing meal, your eyes will involuntarily dilate. You may also know that your pupils dilate when you are sleeping.

What are other things that might cause your eyes to dilate? Have you ever wondered why a typical eye exam usually includes an eye dilation exam?

PROBLEM 1 Horizontal Stretching and Compressing

Now, let's explore the effect of the B- value in the transformational function $g(x) = Af(B(x - C)) + D$. The constant B is a multiplier.

Notice the B-value is on the inside of the function, so which values will be affected: x or y?

1. Compare the graph of $p(x) = x^2$ with $q(x) = (2x)^2$.

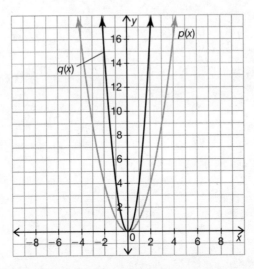

a. Analyze the table of values that correspond to the graph.

x	p(x)	q(x)
0	0	0
1	1	4
2	4	16
3	9	36
4	16	64
5	25	100
6	36	144

Notice when $p(x) = 4$ that $x = 2$, but when $q(x) = 4$ that $x = 1$.

Circle other instances where the y-values for each function are the same. Then, list all the points where $p(x)$ and $q(x)$ have the same y-value.

b. How do the x-values compare when the y-values are the same?

A **horizontal dilation** is a type of transformation that stretches or compresses the entire graph. **Horizontal stretching** is the stretching of a graph away from the y-axis. **Horizontal compression** is the squeezing of a graph towards the y-axis.

Think about how $p(x)$ was transformed to create $q(x)$.

c. Complete the statement.

The function $q(x)$ is a _____ of $p(x)$ by a

factor of _____ .

d. How does the factor of stretching or compression compare to the B-value in $q(x)$?

2. Now, let's compare the graph of $p(x) = x^2$ with $r(x) = p\left(\dfrac{1}{2}x\right)$.

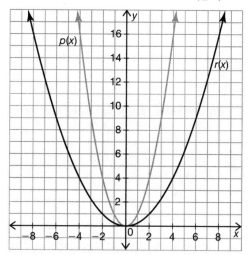

a. Analyze the table of values that correspond to the graph.

x	p(x)	r(x)
0	0	0
1	1	0.25
2	4	1
3	9	2.25
4	16	4
5	25	6.25
6	36	9

Circle instances where the y-values for each function are the same. Then, list all the points where $p(x)$ and $r(x)$ have the same y-value. The first instance has been circled for you.

b. How do the *x*-values compare when the *y*-values are the same?

c. Complete the statement.

The function *r*(x) is a _____ of *p*(x) by a factor of _____.

d. How does the factor of stretching or compression compare to the *B*-value in *q*(x)?

Compared with the graph of *y* = *f*(x), the graph of *y* = *f*(Bx) is:

- horizontally compressed by a factor of $\frac{1}{|B|}$ if $|B| > 1$.
- horizontally stretched by a factor of $\frac{1}{|B|}$ if $0 < |B| < 1$.

You can use reference points to graph the function $d(x) = f\left(\frac{1}{3}x\right)$ when $f(x) = x^2$.

From *d*(x) you know that $C = 0$, $D = 0$, and $B = \frac{1}{3}$. The vertex for *d*(x) is (0, 0).

Notice $0 < |B| < 1$ so the graph will horizontally stretch by a factor of $\frac{1}{\frac{1}{3}}$ or 3.

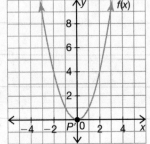
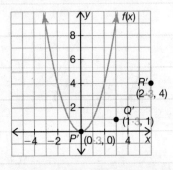
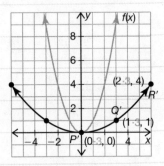

The function *f*(x) is shown. First plot the new vertex (*C*, *D*). This point establishes the new set of axes.

Next, think about *B*. To plot *Q′* move right 1 · 3 units and up 1 unit from the vertex because all *x*-coordinates are being stretched by a factor of 3. To plot *R′* start at the vertex and move to the right 2 · 3 units and go up 4 units.

Finally, use symmetry to complete the graph.

3. List the corresponding points on $d(x)$ for the given points on $f(x)$ in the worked example.

$f(x)$	$d(x)$
(x, y)	
$(-3, 9)$	
$(-2, 4)$	
$(-1, 1)$	
$(0, 0)$	
$(1, 1)$	
$(2, 4)$	
$(3, 9)$	
$(4, 16)$	

4. In the worked example, you analyzed $d(x) = f\left(\frac{1}{3}x\right)$ when $f(x) = x^2$.

   a. If you were asked to graph $h(x) = f(3x)$, describe how the graph would change.

   b. List the corresponding points on $h(x)$ for the given points on $f(x)$.

$f(x)$	$h(x)$
(x, y)	
$(0, 0)$	
$(1, 1)$	
$(2, 4)$	
$(3, 9)$	

5. Analyze the graphs shown on the coordinate plane. Label each graph shown with its corresponding function.

   a. $m(x) = \left(\frac{1}{4}x\right)^2$

   b. $v(x) = (3x)^2$

   c. $p(x) = \left(\frac{1}{3}x\right)^2$

   d. $g(x) = \left(\frac{1}{2}x\right)^2$

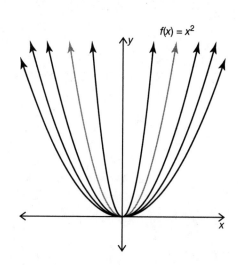

Now that you have studied how $B > 0$ affects the graph of a quadratic function, you will investigate what happens when $B < 0$.

6. Based on what you know about how $A < 0$ values affect the graph of x^2, make a conjecture about how you think $B < 0$ values will affect the graph of x^2.

7. List the corresponding points on $m(x)$ for the given points on $f(x)$.

$f(x) = x^2$		$m(x) = f(-x)$	
	(x, y)		$(-x, y)$
A	$(-3, 9)$	A'	
B	$(-2, 4)$	B'	
C	$(-1, 1)$	C'	
D	$(0, 0)$	D'	
E	$(1, 1)$	E'	
F	$(2, 4)$	F'	
G	$(3, 9)$	G'	

8. Plot and label the points of $f(x)$ and $m(x)$ on the two coordinate planes.

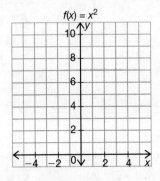
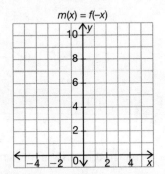

9. Analyze the graphs in Question 8.

  a. What do you notice about the graphs?

  b. What do you notice about the corresponding points in $f(x)$ and $m(x)$?

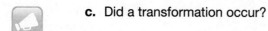

c. Did a transformation occur?

10. Given $f(x) = (x - 5)^2 + 3$.

a. Sketch $d(x) = f(-x)$. Then label A' and B' on your sketch.

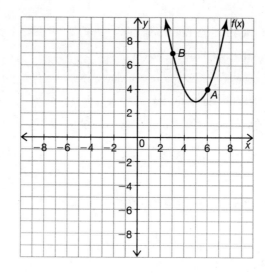

b. Write the function for $d(x)$ by substituting $(-x)$ into $f(x)$. Show all your work.

Compared with the graph of $y = f(x)$, the graph of $y = f(Bx)$ is:

- compressed horizontally by a factor of $\dfrac{1}{|B|}$ if $|B| > 1$.
- stretched horizontally by a factor of $\dfrac{1}{|B|}$ if $0 < |B| < 1$.
- reflected across the y-axis if $B < 0$.

11. Given $y = f(x)$, write the coordinate notation represented in $y = Af(B(x - C)) + D$.

$(x, y) \rightarrow$ _____

12. Connor and Jocelyn each describe the effects of the graph of $d(x) = f(3x + 12)$ when $f(x) = x^2$.

 Connor

$d(x) = f(3x + 12)$

$d(x) = f(3(x + 4))$

The B-value is 3 so the graph will have a horizontal compression of $\frac{1}{3}$. The C value is -4, so the vertex will be shifted 4 units to the left at $(-4, 0)$.

 Jocelyn

$d(x) = f(3x + 12)$

The B-value is 3 so the graph will have a horizontal compression of $\frac{1}{3}$. The C-value is -12, so the vertex will be shifted 12 units to the left at $(-12, 0)$.

a. Explain how Jocelyn incorrectly described the graph of $d(x)$.

b. Use transformations to sketch the graph of $d(x) = f(3(x + 4))$.

$f(x)$	$d(x)$
(0, 0)	
(1, 1)	
(2, 4)	

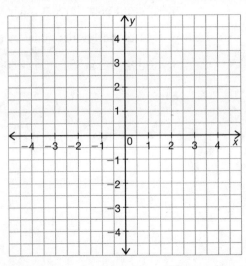

c. Rewrite $d(x)$ in terms of x.

> **Connor**
>
> I can rewrite the function $d(x)$ in terms of x in different ways.
>
> $d(x) = (3x + 12)^2$ or
>
> $d(x) = (3(x + 4))^2$ or
>
> $d(x) = 9(x + 4)^2$

Explain Connor's reasoning.

d. Use transformations to sketch the graph of $d(x) = 9(x + 4)^2$.

f(x)	d(x)
(0, 0)	
(1, 1)	
(2, 4)	

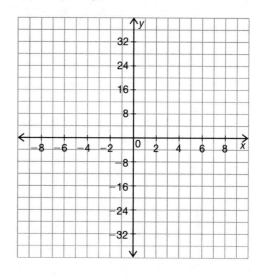

e. Use a graphing calculator to verify that your sketch for $d(x) = f(3(x + 4))$ given $f(x) = x^2$ and $d(x) = 9(x + 4)^2$ is the same.

Use the TABLE feature and analyze each table of values.

f. Why does it make sense that a quadratic function written in transformation notation with a B-value of 3 would produce the same graph as a quadratic function with an A-value of 9?

Talk the Talk

1. Complete the table to describe the graph of each function as a transformation on $y = f(x)$.

Function Form	Equation Information	Description of Transformation of Graph
$y = f(x) + D$	$D > 0$	
	$D < 0$	
$y = f(x - C)$	$C > 0$	
	$C < 0$	
$y = Af(x)$	$|A| > 1$	
	$0 < |A| < 1$	
	$A < 0$	
$y = f(Bx)$	$|B| > 1$	
	$0 < |B| < 1$	
	$B < 0$	

4

2. Given $y = f(x)$, sketch $m(x) = -f(x)$. Describe the transformations you performed.

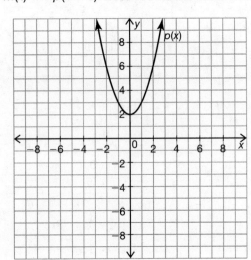

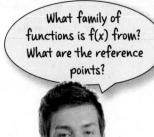

What family of functions is $f(x)$ from? What are the reference points?

3. Given $y = p(x)$, sketch $m(x) = -p(x + 3)$. Describe the transformations you performed.

4. Write *m(x)* in terms of *d(x)*.

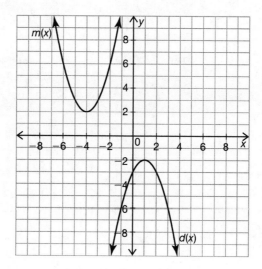

5. Write *m(x)* in terms of *k(x)*.

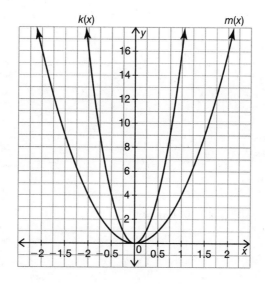

6. Given the graph of $f(x)$, sketch $g(x) = 3f(x + 1) - 6$ on the coordinate plane shown.

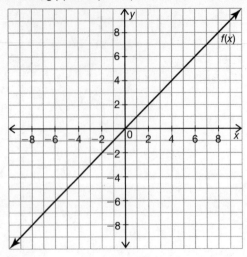

7. Given the graph of $f(x)$, sketch $g(x) = f(x - 2) + 3$ on the coordinate plane shown.

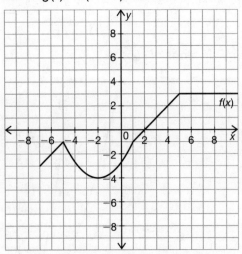

8. Given the graph of $f(x)$, sketch $m(x) = f(-x)$ on the coordinate plane shown. Label A'.

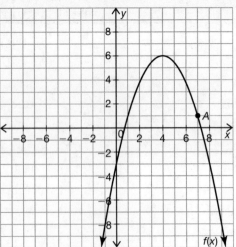

 Be prepared to share your solutions and methods.

What's the Point?
Deriving Quadratic Functions

LEARNING GOALS

In this lesson, you will:

- Determine how many points are necessary to create a unique quadratic equation.
- Derive a quadratic equation given a variety of information using reference points.
- Derive a quadratic equation given three points using a system of equations.
- Derive a quadratic equation given three points using a graphing calculator to perform a quadratic regression.

No matter where you go to see professional baseball in the United States, the dimensions of the infield are all the same. The bases will always be ninety feet apart, and the pitcher's mound is 60.6 feet from home plate. The outfield, however, is a much different story! In fact, baseball is unique in that outfield dimensions, foul area, and outfield walls can be different depending on where the game is being played. For example, the distance from home plate to the right field wall in old Yankee Stadium was actually closer to home plate than its left field wall, making their left-handed power hitters very happy.

Have you ever seen an outfielder jump high above the left field wall to catch a potential homerun? They won't be able to do this in Boston, where the left field wall is 37 feet tall—earning the nickname "the Green Monster."

The dimensions of the field aren't the only differences you will find from stadium to stadium. Dodger Stadium in Los Angeles is built into a mountain side called Chavez Ravine. Turner Field in Atlanta has an arcade area called Scouts Alley. Coors Field in Denver is one mile above sea level that allows the fly balls to travel much further than they normally would because of the thin, dry air. The outfield of PNC Park in Pittsburgh opens up along the Monongahela River, making the city's beautiful skyline visible to all spectators.

Have you ever been to a Major League Baseball game? Did you notice anything unique about the stadium?

1. Consider the family of linear functions. Use the given point(s) to sketch possible solutions.

   a. How many lines can you draw through point *A*?

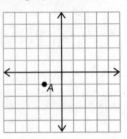

   b. How many lines can you draw through both points *A* and *B*?

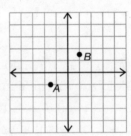

   c. How many lines can you draw through all points *A*, *B*, and *C*?

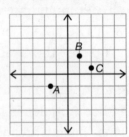

2. What is the minimum number of points you need to draw a unique line?

3. Consider the family of quadratic functions. Use the given point(s) to sketch possible solutions.

a. How many parabolas can you draw through point A?

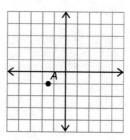

b. How many parabolas can you draw through both points A and B?

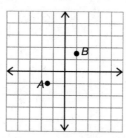

c. How many parabolas can you draw through all points A, B, and C?

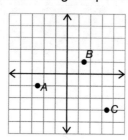

4. Use each coordinate plane and the given information to draw possible parabolas for Examples A through J.

If there is more than one parabola, draw it.

Example A

Given information: The vertex is $(-3, 4)$.

Sketch:

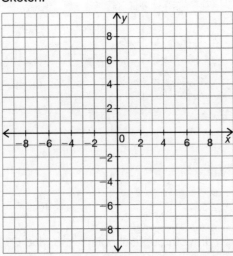

Example B

Given information: The vertex is $(-3, 4)$ and $(-4, 1)$ is a point on the parabola.

Sketch:

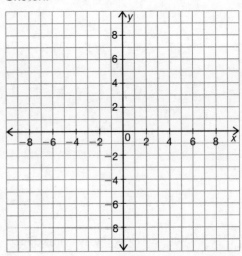

Example C

Given information: The vertex is (3, −2) and one of the two x-intercepts is (4, 0).

Sketch:

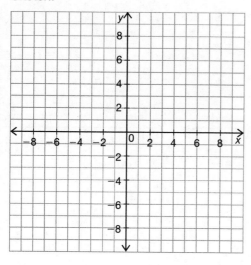

Example D

Given information: The parabola has exactly one x-intercept at (−4, 0) and a y-intercept at (0, 4).

Sketch:

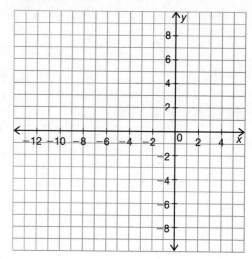

Example E

Given information: The x-intercepts are (−2, 0) and (2, 0).

Sketch:

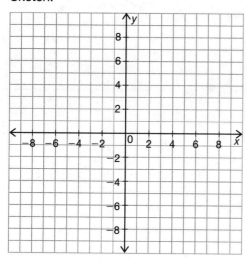

Example F

Given information: The x-intercepts are (−2, 0) and (2, 0), and (−1, −6) is a point on the parabola.

Sketch:

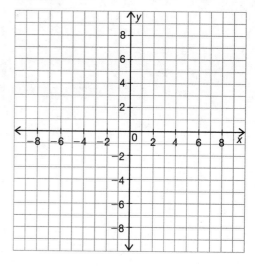

Example G

Given information: The axis of symmetry is $x = -5$ and $(-3, 6)$ is a point on the parabola.

Sketch:

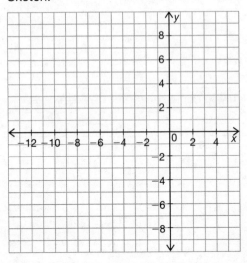

Example H

Given information: The axis of symmetry is $x = -5$, and $(-3, 6)$ and $(1, -10)$ are two points on the parabola.

Sketch:

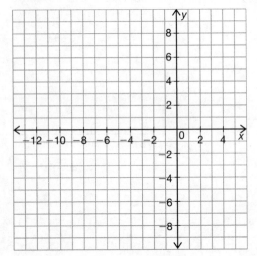

Example I

Given information: Three points on the parabola are $(2, 2)$, $(3, 4)$, and $(4, 6)$.

Sketch:

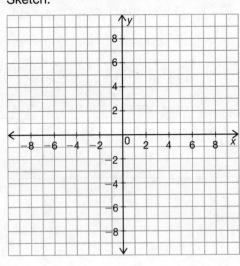

Example J

Given information: Three points on the parabola are $(-4, -8)$, $(0, 8)$, and $(7, -2.5)$.

Sketch:

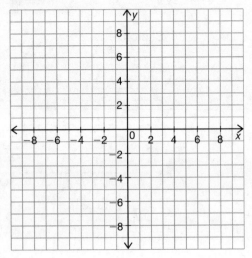

5. Review your work in Question 4.

   a. List the example(s) in which you could draw more than one parabola. How many points were you given for the example(s) you listed?

b. List the example(s) in which you could draw only one parabola. How many points were you given for the example(s) you listed?

c. List the example(s) in which you could not draw a parabola. What did you notice that was different from the examples in which you were able to draw one or more parabolas?

6. Consider the examples in which you could draw only one parabola.

    a. Enter the example letter (A through J) and the given information in the appropriate columns of the table shown.

    b. For each example you listed, did you use the given information to determine any other points so that you could draw the parabola? If yes, enter the number of additional points you used in the appropriate column.

    c. Enter the total number of points you used to draw each parabola in the appropriate column.

Information that Determines A Unique Parabola				
Example	**Given Information**	**Number of Points Given**	**Number of Additional Points**	**Total Number of Points**

7. Summarize your results from Questions 1 through 6 to write a rule for the total number of points needed to determine a unique parabola.

4

Now that you learned how to determine a unique graph of a quadratic function, let's explore ways to write the function.

To write the quadratic function you will need to use the reference points and consider the vertical distance between each point. The basic quadratic function, the reference points, and the vertical distance between those points is shown.

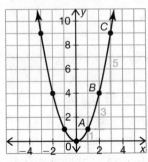

You can use reference points and the factored form of a quadratic function to write the function for the graph explained in Example F. The x-intercepts are (−2, 0) and (2, 0), and (−1, −6) is a point on the parabola.

First, determine the axis of symmetry.
The axis of symmetry must be directly in the middle of the two x-intercepts.

$$x = \frac{r_1 + r_2}{2} = \frac{-2 + 2}{2}$$

$$= \frac{0}{2} = 0$$

The axis of symmetry is x = 0.

Plot the points and label the axis of symmetry on a coordinate plane.

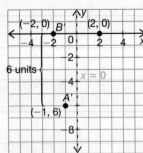

Point B′ is two units away from the axis of symmetry, therefore corresponds to reference point B on the basic function.

Point A′ is one unit away from the axis of symmetry, therefore corresponds to reference point A on the basic function.

Next, determine the a-value.

In the basic quadratic function, the vertical distance between reference point A and B is 3 units. The distance between A′ and B′ is 6 or 3 × 2 units, therefore a = 2.

You now know the values of r_1, r_2, and a, so you can create the unique quadratic function.

$$f(x) = a(x − r_1)(x − r_2)$$
$$f(x) = 2(x − 2)(x + 2)$$

1. Brayden, Max, and Ian are each writing quadratic functions that must satisfy the given information: x-intercepts at (3,0) and (9,0).

Brayden

I know the axis of symmetry is $x = 6$ because it is in the middle of the two x-intercepts. I substituted in the values of x and y for the point $(9, 0)$ that is on the parabola to complete the vertex form.

$$f(x) = a(x - h)^2 + k$$
$$0 = a(3 - 6)^2 + 9$$
$$0 = a(-3)^2 + 9$$
$$0 = 9a + 9$$
$$-9 = 9a$$
$$a = -1$$
Therefore $f(x) = -1(x - 6)^2 + 9$

Max

I know the values for r_1 and r_2. So, all I need is the a-value. I randomly choose an a-value of 4. The function is:

$$f(x) = 4(x - 3)(x - 9)$$

Ian

I created a graph to model the situation, and choose to add the point $(4, -10)$.

I know that the given point $(3, 0)$ must be the C' because it is 3 units away from the axis of symmetry. By the same reasoning my new point must be B' because it is only 2 units away from the axis of symmetry. If the a-value was 1, the vertical distance between B' and C' would be 5. In this graph the vertical distance is 2×5, therefore the a-value must be 2.

The function is:

$$f(x) = 2(x - 3)(x - 9)$$

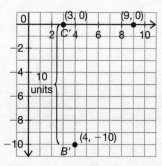

Who's method and quadratic function is correct? Explain your reasoning.

2. Use your knowledge of reference points to write a quadratic function for the examples previously identified as unique parabolas in Problem 1. If it is not possible to write a function, state why not.

a. Example B

Given: Vertex $(-3, 4)$; point $(-4, 1)$

$f(x) = $ _____

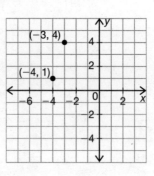

b. Example C

Given: Vertex $(3, -2)$; one of two x-intercepts $(4, 0)$

$f(x) = $ _____

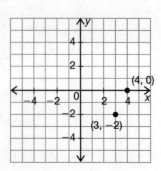

c. Example J

Given: Points $(-4, -8)$, $(0, 8)$, $(7, -2.5)$

$f(x) =$ _____

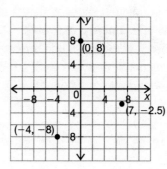

Technology Whiz

Using reference points and the axis of symmetry to write the equation of a quadratic function is an efficient method to use when given certain points. However, this method will not always work. As you saw in Example J of Problem 2, if you do not know the axis of symmetry, you cannot use reference points. You can use a graphing calculator or systems of equations as two other methods to write quadratic functions.

> Make sure you set the appropriate viewing window to view the graph.

You can use a graphing calculator to determine a quadratic regression equation given three points on the parabola.

Step 1: Diagnostics must be turned on so that all needed data is displayed. Press **2ⁿᵈ CATALOG** to display the catalog. Scroll to **DiagnosticOn** and press **ENTER**. Then press **ENTER** again. The calculator should display the word **Done**.

> If there is already data in your L1 list, highlight the heading L1, Press CLEAR, then Press ENTER to delete it.

Step 2: Press **STAT** and then press **ENTER** to select **1:Edit**. In the **L1** column, enter the x-values by typing each value followed by **ENTER**. Use the right arrow key to move to the **L2** column. **ENTER** the y-values.

Step 3: Press **STAT** and use the right arrow key to show the **CALC** menu. Choose **5:QuadReg**. Press Enter. The values for a, b, and c will be displayed.

Step 4: To have the calculator graph the exact equation, press **Y=**, **VARS**, **5:Statistics**, scroll right to **EQ**, press **1:RegEQ**, **GRAPH**.

1. Use a graphing calculator to determine the quadratic equation for Example J.

2. Use a graphing calculator to determine the quadratic function for each set of three points that lie on a parabola.

   a. points $(-1, 36)$, $(1, 12)$, and $(2, 6)$

   b. points $(0, 2)$, $(-1, 9)$ and $(3, 5)$

   c. points $(2, 3)$, $(3, 13)$ and $(4, 29)$

3. Van McSlugger needs one more homerun to advance to the next round of the home run derby. On the last pitch, he takes a swing and makes contact. Initially, he hits the ball at 5 feet above the ground. At 32 feet from home plate his ball was 23.7 feet in the air, and at 220 feet from home plate his ball was 70 feet in the air.

   a. Draw a figure to represent this situation. Include any known data points.

   b. Use a graphing calculator to write a function for the height of the ball in terms of its horizontal distance to home plate. Round to the nearest thousandth.

   c. If Van's ball needs to travel a distance of 399 feet in order to get the homerun, did he succeed? Explain why or why not.

   d. What was the maximum height of Van's baseball?

All About the Algebra

You know that the method of using reference points to determine a quadratic equation does not always work. You know how to use a graphing calculator to create the equation, but what happened before the graphing calculator? What if you don't have graphing calculator, or needed to explain to somebody how to write the equation?

You can use algebra to solve! You can set up and solve systems of equations to determine a quadratic equation.

You now know that you need a minimum of 3 non-linear points to create a unique parabola. In order to create an equation to represent the parabola, you must use systems of equations.

Consider the three points $A(2, 1)$, $B(-1, -2)$, and $C(3, -10)$.

First, create a quadratic equation in the standard form $y = ax^2 + bx + c$ for each of the points:

Point A: $\begin{aligned} 1 &= a(2)^2 + b(2) + c \\ 1 &= 4a + 2b + c \end{aligned}$ Equation A: $1 = 4a + 2b + c$

Point B: $\begin{aligned} -2 &= a(-1)^2 + b(-1) + c \\ -2 &= a - b + c \end{aligned}$ Equation B: $-2 = a - b + c$

Point C: $\begin{aligned} -10 &= a(3)^2 + b(3) + c \\ -10 &= 9a + 3b + c \end{aligned}$ Equation C: $-10 = 9a + 3b + c$

Now, use elimination and substitution to solve for a, b, and c.

STEP 1: Subtract Equation B from A:

$$\begin{aligned} 1 &= 4a + 2b + c \\ -(-2 &= a - b + c) \\ \hline 3 &= 3a + 3b \end{aligned}$$

STEP 2: Subtract Equation C from B:

$$\begin{aligned} -10 &= 9a + 3b + c \\ -(-2 &= a - b + c) \\ \hline -8 &= 8a + 4b \end{aligned}$$

STEP 3: Solve the equation from Step 1 in terms of a.

$$\begin{aligned} 3 &= 3a + 3b \\ 3 - 3b &= 3a \\ 1 - b &= a \end{aligned}$$

STEP 4: Substitute the value for a into the equation from Step 2.

$$\begin{aligned} -8 &= 8(1 - b) + 4b \\ -8 &= 8 - 4b \\ 16 &= 4b \\ 4 &= b \end{aligned}$$

STEP 5: Substitute the value for b into the equation from Step 3.

$$\begin{aligned} a &= 1 - (4) \\ a &= -3 \end{aligned}$$

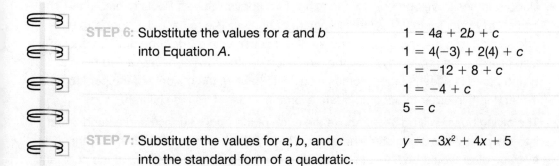

STEP 6: Substitute the values for a and b into Equation A.

$1 = 4a + 2b + c$
$1 = 4(-3) + 2(4) + c$
$1 = -12 + 8 + c$
$1 = -4 + c$
$5 = c$

STEP 7: Substitute the values for a, b, and c into the standard form of a quadratic.

$y = -3x^2 + 4x + 5$

1. Create a system of equations and use algebra to create a quadratic equation with points $(-1, 5)$, $(0, 3)$, and $(3, 9)$.

2. Happy Homes Development Company has hired Splish Splash Pools to create the community pool for their new development of homes. The rectangular pool is to have one section with a 4-foot depth, and another section with a 9-foot depth. The pool will also have a diving board. By law, the regulation depth of water necessary to have a diving board is 9 feet. Happy Homes would like to have the majority of the pool to be a 4-feet depth in order to accommodate a large number of young children.

The diving board will be 3 feet above the edge of the pool's surface and extend 5 feet into the pool. After doing some research, Splish Splash Pools determined that the average diver would be 5 feet in the air when he is 8 feet from the edge of the pool, and 6 feet in the air when he is 10 feet from the edge of the pool. According to this dive model, what is the minimum length of 9 foot depth section of the pool?

   a. Fill in the diagram with all known information.

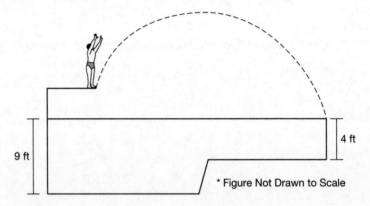

9 ft

4 ft

* Figure Not Drawn to Scale

   b. Write a quadratic equation in standard form for each of the points you know.

c. Use substitution and elimination to solve the system of equations for variables *a*, *b*, and *c*.

d. Use your new equation to determine the minimum length of the 9 foot depth section of the pool.

 Be prepared to share your solutions and methods.

Now It's Getting Complex . . . But It's Really Not Difficult!

Complex Number Operations

"Let me hear the downbeat!" might be something you hear the lead singer tell the band to start a song during a performance. In fact for centuries, bands, ensembles, barber shop quartets, and orchestras relied on tempo and beats to sync up with other band members. Well, this is true for band members today, but there is also music that doesn't have any band members—but a single musician mixing it up on turntables or on a laptop! Of course, these solo musicians are called DJs who have been mixing it since the late 1960s.

The cornerstone of almost any DJ's music is the art of sampling. Sampling is taking a portion or a "sample" of one sound recording and repurposing it into another song. One of the most common samples is taking the drum beats. Many DJs will take four measures of drum beats (with each measure having 4 beats per measure), and reuse it to become the spine of their new piece. Sometimes those four drum-beat measures are repeated for an entire piece—and sometimes these pieces can last 20 to 30 minutes in duration with the DJ infusing other samples of vinyl noise, ambient sound effects, record scratches, and lyrics.

Even more recently, artists have been using technology to create mashups. Mashups generally use two or more pre-recorded songs (not just samples, but entirely mixed songs) and arranging them together to create a new musical piece. Do you think that mashups use this same concept of 4 measures of music to create new musical pieces? Why do you think "4" is so special in creating music?

So far within this course, you have worked within the set of real numbers and determined real number solutions. Remember, the set of real numbers includes the sets of rational and irrational numbers.

1. Consider the equation $x^2 = -1$.
   Is there a real number solution to this equation?
   Explain why or why not.

> So if it's not a real number, does that mean it's a fake number?

The imaginary number *i* is a number such that $i^2 = -1$. Because no real number exists such that its square is equal to a negative number, the number *i* is not a part of the real number system.

2. If $i^2 = -1$, what is the value of *i*?

4

3. Use the values of *i* and i^2 and the properties of exponents to calculate each power of *i*. Enter your results in the table and show your work.

Powers of *i*			
$i =$	$i^2 =$	$i^3 =$	$i^4 =$
$i^5 =$	$i^6 =$	$i^7 =$	$i^8 =$
$i^9 =$	$i^{10} =$	$i^{11} =$	$i^{12} =$

> Use previously calculated powers of *i* to calculate the next power of *i*.

4. Describe any patterns you see in the table.

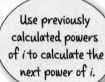

5. Tristan, Kira, and Libby calculated the power i^{15} using different methods as shown.

   a. Explain why each student's method is correct.

Tristan

$i^{15} = (i^4)^3 \cdot i^3$

$= (1)^3(-\sqrt{-1})$

$= 1(-\sqrt{-1})$

$= -\sqrt{-1}$

Kira

The exponent of i^{15} is 15. When I divide 15 by 4, I have a remainder of 3 I know $i^3 = -\sqrt{-1}$. So, $i^{15} = i^3 = -\sqrt{-1}$.

> What's so special about multiplying by i^4?

Libby

$i^{15} = i \cdot i \cdot i \cdot i \cdot i \cdot i \cdot i \cdot i \cdot i \cdot i \cdot i \cdot i \cdot i \cdot i \cdot i$

$= \underbrace{\sqrt{-1} \cdot \sqrt{-1}}_{-1} \cdot \underbrace{\sqrt{-1} \cdot \sqrt{-1}}_{-1} \cdot \underbrace{\sqrt{-1} \cdot \sqrt{-1}}_{-1} \cdot \underbrace{\sqrt{-1} \cdot \sqrt{-1}}_{-1} \cdot \underbrace{\sqrt{-1} \cdot \sqrt{-1}}_{-1} \cdot \underbrace{\overline{-1} \cdot \sqrt{-1}}_{-1} \cdot \underbrace{\sqrt{-1} \cdot \sqrt{-1}}_{-1} \cdot \sqrt{-1}$

$= -1 \cdot \sqrt{-1}$

$= -1\sqrt{-1}$

   b. If you had to calculate i^{99}, whose method would you use and why?

6. Explain how to calculate any integer power of i.

7. Calculate each power of i.

a. $i^{93} =$

b. $i^{206} =$

c. $i^{400} =$

d. $i^{-2} =$

Here's a hint for part (e): Use the properties of exponents and your answer to part (d) to write a equivalent expression for i^{-1}.

Now that you know about i, you can rewrite expressions involving negative roots. For any positive real number n, the **principal square root of a negative number,** $-n$, is defined by $\sqrt{-n} = i\sqrt{n}$.

Determine the value of $\sqrt{-75}$.

$$\sqrt{-75} = \sqrt{(-1)(75)}$$
$$= \sqrt{-1} \cdot \sqrt{75}$$
$$= i\sqrt{25 \cdot 3}$$
$$= 5\sqrt{3}\,i$$

So, use the definition of the principal square root of a negative number before performing operations!

8. Analyze Georgette's work.

👎 **Georgette**

$$\sqrt{-32} = -\sqrt{32}$$
$$= -\sqrt{16(2)}$$
$$= -4\sqrt{2}$$

Explain why she is incorrect.

9. Jen and Tami each rewrote the expression $\sqrt{-4} \cdot \sqrt{-4}$.

Jen	Tami
$\sqrt{-4} \cdot \sqrt{-4}$	$\sqrt{-4} \cdot \sqrt{-4}$
$= \sqrt{(-4)(-4)}$	$= 2i \cdot 2i$
$= \sqrt{16}$	$= 4i^2$
$= 4$	$= -4$

Who's correct? Explain the error in the other student's reasoning.

10. Rewrite each expression using i.

    a. $\sqrt{64} - \sqrt{-63} =$

    b. $\sqrt{-13} + 10 =$

    c. $\dfrac{1 - \sqrt{-44}}{2} =$

4

The **set of imaginary numbers** is the set of all numbers written in the form $a + bi$, where a and b are real numbers and b is not equal to 0. A **pure imaginary number** is a number of the form bi, where b is not equal to 0.

Why should I care about numbers that are imaginary?

1. Write the imaginary number i in the form $a + bi$. What are the values of a and b?

2. Give an example of a pure imaginary number.

Imaginary numbers actually have applications in real life. They are used in the scientific fields of electromagnetism, fluid dynamics, and quantum mechanics, just to name a few!

3. Can a number be both real and imaginary? Explain why or why not.

The **set of complex numbers** is the set of all numbers written in the form $a + bi$, where a and b are real numbers. The term a is called the **real part of a complex number**, and the term bi is called the **imaginary part of a complex number**.

4. Identify whether each number is a complex number. Explain your reasoning.

   a. i

   b. 3

   c. -5.5216

   d. $\pi + 3.2i$

5. What is the difference between a complex number and an imaginary number?

6. Create a diagram to show the relationship between each set of numbers shown.

- complex numbers
- imaginary numbers
- integers
- irrational numbers
- natural numbers
- rational numbers
- real numbers
- whole numbers

7. Use the word box to complete each statement. Explain your reasoning.

always	sometimes	never

a. If a number is an imaginary number, then it is _____ a complex number.

b. If a number is a complex number, then it is _____ an imaginary number.

c. If a number is a real number, then it is _____ a complex number.

d. If a number is a real number, then it is _____ an imaginary number.

e. If a number is a complex number, then it is _____ a real number.

PROBLEM 3 Call the Doctor, Stat! It's Time to Operate!

You know how to perform the basic operations of addition, subtraction, multiplication, and division on the set of real numbers. You can also perform these operations on the set of complex numbers.

When operating with complex numbers involving *i*, combine like terms by treating *i* as a variable (even though it is a constant).

1. Simplify each expression. Show your work.

   a. $(3 + 2i) - (1 - 6i) =$

   b. $4i + 3 - 6 + i - 1 =$

   c. $5i(3 - 2i) =$

   d. $(5 + 3i)(2 - 3i) =$

2. Determine each product.

   a. $(2 + i)(2 - i) =$ **b.** $\left(\frac{1}{2} + i\right)\left(\frac{1}{2} - i\right) =$

   c. $(3 + 2i)(3 - 2i) =$ **d.** $(1 - 3i)(1 + 3i) =$

   e. What do you notice about each product?

4